ULTIMATE
QUIZ BOOK

BULLSEYE™

igloobooks

igloobooks

Published in 2017
by Igloo Books Ltd
Cottage Farm
Sywell
NN6 0BJ
www.igloobooks.com

HUN001 0717
2 4 6 8 10 9 7 5 3 1
ISBN 978-1-78557-282-1

Cover designed by Charlie Wood-Penn
Interiors designed by Simon Parker
Edited by Jasmin Peppiatt

Printed and manufactured in China

Contents

You Can't Beat A Bit Of Bully!

With thousands of viewers tuning in every week, Bullseye was a big hit. Hosted by Jim Bowen, who has recently been voted the nation's favourite television host, the show brought viewers over ten years of fantastic quizzes, championed by the famous Bully. With memorable catchphrases and comical prizes to be won, this show wasn't to be missed.

Contestants would go head-to-head, competing to beat Bully in various rounds of quizzes.

Now you can compete against family and friends! Packed full of quizzes and thousands of questions, this Ultimate Bullseye Quiz Book will test your knowledge and see if you can beat Bully. If you're not quick off the mark, you may win nothing but your bus fare home!

Super, smashing, great!

2000s Music

1. What 2000s hit contained the line, 'Nobody told me it feels so good, Nobody said you would be so beautiful'?

2. What was Take That's big comeback hit in 2006?

3. Which 2000s music star was killed in a car accident on April 25th 2002?

4. Which *X Factor* winner had the final No. 1 of the 2000s?

5. Who released the album *Let Go* in 2003?

6. Who's debut album in 2000 was called *Born to do it*?

7. What was Oasis' last UK No. 1?

8. What was DJ Pied Piper's biggest hit?

9. Which Rihanna song spent 10 weeks at No. 1 in 2007?

10. Wyclef Jean was a featured artist on what 2006 mega hit?

11. Alex Turner was the lead singer with which group?

12. Who won the first series of Fame Academy?

13. Who were the members of N-Dubz?

14. In which year did Hear'say have their first hit?

15. Who featured on Eminem's hit *Stan*?

16. Which group had the most UK number ones of the 2000s?

17. What did JLS stand for?

18. Members of which 80s band wrote the Atomic Kitten hit *Whole Again*?

19. Which band comprised Claire, Faye, Lisa, Ian and Lee?

20. Who had a hit with *That's Not My Name*?

"Now the cash you won for charity earlier... that's safe."

50/50

1. Has Al Gore won an Oscar?

2. Is Chesterfield closer geographically to Sheffield or Derby?

3. Is Arbroath on the East Coast or the West Coast of Scotland?

4. Who was born first, Ant or Dec?

5. What side of the road do they drive on in the United Arab Emirates?

6. Is the London Dungeon tourist attraction on the South or the North of the Thames?

7. Which country has the larger land area, USA or Canada?

8. Who is older, Lorraine Kelly or Ulrika Jonsson?

9. Who was born first, Chuck Norris or Bruce Lee?

10. What has more bones, a human or a mouse?

11. Who is older, Boris Johnson or David Cameron?

12. What is older, the state of Israel or the NHS?

13. Was the Bank of England founded by an Englishman or a Scotsman?

14. Is sub-letting your council house a criminal offence?

15. Who have won the Spanish league more times, Real Madrid or Barcelona?

16. Who won the 2016 Boat Race?

17. Have there been over 1000 or under 1000 episodes of *Come Dine With Me*?

18. Who was older, Laurel or Hardy?

19. Who is older, Robert de Niro or Al Pacino?

20. As of April 2017, is Doris Day still alive?

"Stay out of the black and into the red, nothing in this game for two in a bed."

60s Music

1. What was Doris Day's only UK music hit of the 1960s?

2. Which Welsh singer is best known for the hit *Those Were the Days*?

3. Who was the 'King of Skiffle'?

4. What was the name of the record label founded by The Beatles in 1968?

5. What group backed Cliff Richard on numerous 60s hits?

6. Who had a hit with *Let's Twist Again* in 1961?

7. In which 60s song does Frank Sinatra fade out singing 'doo-be-do-be-doo'?

8. Which British comedian gave us one of the biggest hits of the 1960s?

9. Who broke records when his first 7 hits all reached the UK Top 5?

10. Which famous band was formed by two Brothers in Muswell Hill, London in 1963?

11. How many UK No. 1s did Jim Reeves have in the 1960s?

12. What was Ray Charles' first UK Top Ten hit?

13. Which 1962 No. 1 was the biggest selling instrumental song of all time?

14. What was The Beatle's first UK number one single?

15. What was Steppenwolf's biggest hit?

16. Which future Eastenders star featured on 60s number one *Come Outside*?

17. Which 60s hit begins, 'The old home town looks the same as I step down from the train'?

18. How is Arnold George Dorsey better known?

19. What 'boys' gave us *Barbara Ann*?

20. Who had a million selling single with *Young Girl*?

"Look at what you could have won."

80s Music

1. Neil from the Young Ones had what No. 2 hit in 1984?

2. How were The Stranglers originally known?

3. Who had a major hit with *Father Figure*?

4. Which song begins with the chant, 'Please, Please Tell Me Now'?

5. What age was Stevie Wonder when he released *I Just Called to Say I Love You*?

6. Two members of Duran Duran formed which Super Group with Robert Palmer?

7. What was the last UK No. 1 of the 80s?

8. Who had a huge hit with *China In Your Hand*?

9. Were Bananarama a duo, a trio or a quartet?

10. Who was the lead singer of Visage?

11. Who had an 80s hit with *Notorious*?

12. What song spent the longest time at No. 1 in the 80s?

13. Which pair made a terrible job of presenting the Brit Awards in 1989?

14. How is Farrokh Bulsara better known?

15. Who was the lead singer of The Bangles?

16. The lyrics, 'lays me down with my mind she runs', are from what hit?

17. 'Six o'clock already, I was just in the middle of a dream' is the opening line of which song?

18. Who was the lead singer of Frankie Goes To Hollywood?

19. What was Samantha Fox's biggest hit?

20. What was Marvin Gaye's first single after leaving Motown?

"And Bully's Special Priiiiize..."

Abbreviations

1. What does the O.J. stand for in O.J. Simpson?

2. In finance, what does FTSE stand for?

3. What does USA stand for?

4. On Twitter, what does FF stand for?

5. What does the J.R.R. stand for in J.R.R. Tolkien?

6. Yasser Arafat was the leader of the PLO. What does PLO stand for?

"Now the cash you won for charity earlier... that's safe."

7. What does VHS stand for?

8. What did J.R. stand for in J.R. Ewing?

9. F.W. de Klerk was the President of South Africa, what did F.W. stand for?

10. What did the P.L. stand for in the name of Mary Poppins author P.L. Travers?

11. What did the H.G. stand for in the name H.G. Wells?

12. What does TBH mean in text speak?

13. What does DNA stand for?

14. What does IMO mean in text speak?

15. What does CSI stand for in the name of the hit TV franchise?

16. What does ICYMI stand for?

17. What did the J.M.W. stand for in the name of artist J.M.W. Turner?

18. In music, what did the band name OMD stand for?

19. What did the country name USSR stand for?

20. What does UCAS stand for?

Actors

1. Who is the youngest actor to win a Best Actor Oscar?

2. Which singer began his acting career in *Memphis Belle*?

3. Who played cross-dressing Klinger in *MASH*?

4. What was Michael Caine's character name in *The Man Who Would Be King*?

5. In which film did Johnny Depp speak only 169 words?

6. Who played Lieutenant Hubert Gruber in *'Allo 'Allo*?

7. At the end of Season Five, who has appeared in the most episodes of *Game of Thrones*?

8. For which film did Dustin Hoffman win his first Oscar?

9. Who had his big break playing the role of Richard Roma in the first American production of David Mamet's play Glengarry Glen Ross, the first of many collaborations with Mamet?

10. In which country was Sid James born?

11. What is Tom Cruise's real name?

12. Who played Howard Hughes in *The Aviator*?

13. Who played He-Man in the 1980s live action movie?

14. What is Michael Keaton's real name?

15. In which film did Charlie Sheen play *Bud Fox*?

16. What are the names of Bruce Lee's children?

17. Which character did Michael Caine play in 5 films?

18. Which giant of the British stage was born on the 22nd May 1907?

19. Which character did Ted Danson play in *Cheers*?

20. Who did Lee Strasberg play in *The Godfather: Part II*?

"Super, smashing, great."

Actresses

1. Which two actors were present on the night Natalie Wood died?

2. Who was Nicole Kidman's first husband?

3. Who played Summer in *500 Days of Summer*?

4. Who was the female lead in *Top Gun*?

5. Who is Michael Madsen's actress sister?

"101 or more with 6 darts for tonight's mystery star prize"

6. Which actress was voted the American Film Institute's 'Screen Legend of the Century'?

7. What is the surname of acting sisters Jemima and Lola?

8. Which actress, born in 1947, has received 6 Oscar nominations?

9. What was Grace Kelly's last film?

10. Which famous actress was married to Bobby Darin?

11. Which Charlie's Angel starred in *The Mask* and *There's Something About Mary*?

12. Who is Bette Midler named after?

13. Who played Jane in the Johnny Weissmuller Tarzan films?

14. Which actress was married to Laurence Olivier from 1940 to 1960?

15. Who starred in *The Godfather* and *Rocky*?

16. In which country was actress Isla Fisher born?

17. Who did Jennifer Aniston marry in 2015?

18. Which character did Jennifer Lawrence play in *The Hunger Games*?

19. Who was the female lead of *Memoirs of an Invisible Man*?

20. In 1995, Kylie Minogue appeared in the movie tie-in to which computer game?

Americanisms

1. What is playtime known as to an American child?

2. What do Americans call a tap?

3. What do Americans call a mobile phone?

4. How would an American refer to a hotel receptionist?

5. If an American 'flipped the bird' what would he be doing?

6. What do Americans call a baby's dummy?

7. What do Americans call a long distance overnight airplane flight?

8. What do Americans call a car boot?

9. What do Americans call clay pigeon shooting?

10. What do Americans call a full stop?

11. What do Americans call draughts?

12. What would Americans call a funeral parlour?

13. What do Americans call nappies?

14. What do Americans call coriander?

15. What do Americans call their trousers?

16. What do Americans call their mum?

17. What do Americans call a state school?

18. If Americans call petrol gas, what do they call natural gas?

19. What do Americans know as the sidewalk?

20. What do Americans call a car park?

"All for the throw of a dart"

Animals 1

1. What is the largest extant member of the deer family?

2. A pullet is a young what?

3. What is a whale's leap out of the water called?

4. What type of animal is Babar?

5. What is the national animal of the USA?

6. What is a young sheep called?

7. What is the opposite of nocturnal?

8. What unit is used to measure the height of horses?

9. What kind of animal is Paddington? Bear

10. What is a female donkey called?

11. How many toes does a rhino have?

12. What is different about a Manx cat?

13. How many wings does a bee have?

14. What word means bear-like?

15. What breed of dog is famous for Alpine rescues?

16. What is the fastest 2 legged animal in the world? Cheetah or Leopard

17. What North American mammal is also known as the Prairie Wolf?

18. A koala is not a bear. What type of animal is it? Mammel

19. Jonathan of the Seychelle Islands is 184 years old. What kind of animal is Jonathan?

20. In what book are threatened species of wildlife recorded?

"Go for your lights"

Animals 2

1. What is generally considered to be the largest type of bear?

2. In animals, what would we call a sustained period of inactivity and low metabolism, usually happening over winter?

3. What could be long-eared, barn or tawny?

4. What is the only breed of dog to be named after a fictional character?

5. What is a male duck called?

6. How many toes does a wolf have?

7. What name is given to a baby crocodile?

8. What name is given to a female dog?

9. What is the 4 letter alternative name for a Killer Whale?

10. A baby guinea pig is called what?

11. What is the name of an otter's home?

12. What type of turtle is noted for its combative disposition?

13. Which animal is key to the legend of the origin of the Roman Civilisation?

14. In the UK, what animals are usually classed as red or grey?

15. What is the largest snake in the world by weight?

16. What C could also be described as a shag?

17. Where on a fish's body are the growth rings scientists use to determine age?

18. What name is given to the edible lining of a cow's stomach?

19. What type of animal is a Bombay Duck?

20. What is the female of a fallow deer called?

"You've got the time it takes for the board to revolve..."

Anything Goes 1

1. What is the unofficial motto of the French Foreign Legion?

2. What do we call a glove which covers the entire hand but does not have separate finger openings?

3. What age was James Dean when he died?

4. If you were 'in the nick' where would you be?

5. Grace Kelly was allegedly a member of what cult group?

6. Which band had a minor hit with *James Dean*?

7. What is a Croydon Facelift?

8. What could be Windsor, Prince Albert or Simple?

"Now the cash you won for charity earlier... that's safe."

9. What is the name of Twitter's blue bird mascot?

10. What name did Amazon give to its series of E-readers?

11. What item of clothing could be a reference to 'a socially awkward person obsessively interested in something'?

12. What actress was discovered in 1937 by a reporter as she sipped a soda in a Hollywood ice cream parlour?

13. What was Marilyn Monroe's bra size?

14. What country's motto is 'Peace, Rain, Prosperity'?

15. Where was Osama Bin Laden supposedly buried?

16. Who supposedly shot JFK?

17. For which baseball team did Joe DiMaggio play?

18. 'Today, Tomorrow and Forever' is the motto of which hated American organisation?

19. In which year was eBay started?

20. Which home movie was a very important part of the Warren Commission's investigation of the shooting of JFK?

Anything Goes 2

1. What was Fred Astaire's real name?

2. Which dating app supposedly registered one billion swipes per day in 2014?

3. What age was Joan Rivers when she died?

4. Henry Ford funded the printing of 500,000 copies of which book in the 1920s?

5. In what state was Marlon Brando born?

6. In fashion, what is an ascot?

"You can't beat a bit of Bully!"

7. What motto was used by Donald Trump during his 2016 Presidential Campaign?

8. What rough, woollen fabric is often coloured Lovat Green?

9. Michael Foot, perhaps unfairly, was criticised for wearing what type of jacket to Remembrance Sunday Ceremonies in 1981?

10. Who was the founder of MegaUpload?

11. What are Winkle Pickers?

12. What name is given to the partners of homosexuals, used to promote the idea that the person is heterosexual?

13. What is the motto of France?

14. Where would a cockney wear gregorys?

15. Which Swedish Prime Minister was assassinated in 1986?

16. In which city are the headquarters of Amazon located?

17. Which company makes the Galaxy S7 mobile phone?

18. What is Julian Assange's controversial website?

19. With whom did Trinny Woodall write a weekly fashion column for *The Daily Telegraph*?

20. Who was the top pin-up girl for GIs during World War II?

Anything Goes 3

1. What is the modern motto of the United States of America?

2. Who are the 'Boys in Blue'?

3. What do Birthers believe?

4. What German star moved away from the world of movies and into cabaret, often appearing in a top hat and tails?

5. What were Joe DiMaggio's last words?

6. Where would you wear gauntlets?

"Remember, you can't beat a bit of Bully!"

7. According to *Forbes Magazine*, how many children did Marlon Brando have?

8. John Hinckley attempted to shoot Ronald Reagan as a means of impressing which actress?

9. What C is a pejorative term for white people, especially poor rural whites in some Southern United States?

10. Which ex-footballer is famous for claiming that the Royal Family are 'shape shifting reptilians'?

11. What is the motto of The Scouts?

12. Which star of the 1931 film *Mata Hari* retired aged 35?

13. Which successful computer game franchise was introduced by Sega in 1991?

14. The first Indian Prime Minister gave his name to what article of clothing?

15. What controversial website was created by Ross Ulbricht?

16. What business are Uber in?

17. If a Geordie is getting 'mortal', what are they doing?

18. How many sections is the world split into on the flag of the UN?

19. What would a cockney do with a dog and bone?

20. What Malaysian Airways flight disappeared over the South China Sea in 2014?

Bits and Pieces 1

1. In what year was The Orange Order founded?

2. What city is the location for most Martin Scorsese films?

3. What nationality is tennis player Jelena Janovic?

4. What star of the 1920s was known as 'The Latin Lover'?

5. What is an Ossuary?

6. What town is the northernmost in England?

7. Who is the leader of North Korea?

8. What natural disaster is measured on the Richter Scale?

9. What is the stimulant in coffee?

10. Who directed *The Deer Hunter*?

11. The phrase 'going down the rabbit hole' is based on which story?

12. Who became Prime Minister at the age of 24?

13. What gifts were given to the Baby Jesus?

14. What shape is produced by bees when constructing a honeycomb?

15. Who directed Madonna's *Vogue* video?

16. Which was the first Motown single to reach No.1 in the US Billboard pop charts?

17. What does *antebellum* mean?

18. What breed of dog is Scooby-Doo?

19. Who directed *Home Alone*?

20. DuPont chemist Wallace Carothers developed what new plastic material in 1930?

"Bully's bellowed you out there!"

Bits and Pieces 2

"101 or more with 6 darts for tonight's mystery star prize"

1. What happened in Folkestone on 3rd March 2009?

2. What colour is Kermit the Frog?

3. What was F. Scott's Fitzgerald's unfinished novel?

4. In which country is the majority of *The Da Vinci Code* set?

5. What is the first foreign country you would reach if you go north of Detroit, Michigan?

6. How many locks are on the Suez Canal?

7. How did Lawrence of Arabia die?

8. What was Bob Hope's signature tune?

9. Which large publisher is part of Rupert Murdoch's News Corp?

10. How many metres in a kilometre?

11. Nawaz Sharif is the Prime Minister of which country?

12. What modern animal did a Mastodon resemble?

13. Which planet's moons include Miranda and Titania?

14. In what year was Stan Lee born?

15. What word is Spanish for sun?

16. What was the name of Sigourney Weaver's character in *Alien*?

17. What was the name of the first dog in space?

18. What road runs from Leeds to Scarborough?

19. Who played Frasier in *Frasier* and *Cheers*?

20. How is the director Rajmund Roman Thierry Polański known?

Bits and Pieces 3

1. Who was the narrator of *Pineapple Dance Studios*?

2. Hepatitis is the inflammation of which of the body's organs?

3. In what country was Queen Elizabeth II when her father died?

4. Who was Bob Hope's partner in the *Road to...* films?

5. What is the more common name for the larynx?

6. Which Texas city is nicknamed 'The Yellow Rose of Texas'?

7. Who is the longest-reigning super-middleweight world champion in history?

8. How was Charles Lutwidge Dodgson better known?

9. Who sang *Something Tells Me I'm Into Something Good*?

"Let's check that with Bully"

10. What state of the USA is known as the Golden State?

11. What did Yankee Doodle stick in his hat?

12. Who discovered penicillin?

13. The Roadrunner is the official bird of which US state?

14. Who did George W. Bush defeat in the 2000 US Election?

15. What is a pallindromic disease?

16. In which film did Liam Neeson say 'I will look for you, I will find you, and I will kill you'?

17. In what year was the film *Taken* released?

18. In 2001, who was wrongly convicted for the murder of Jill Dando?

19. Which 2007 film is believed to be the most profitable film ever made?

20. How is the Eighty Years War also known?

Bits and Pieces 4

1. Who was The Teflon Don?

2. What's the world's largest predatory fish?

3. What 2010 Disney film was based on the story of *Rapunzel*?

4. Who is Lionel Messi named after?

5. What is French for Saint Stephen?

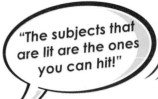

"The subjects that are lit are the ones you can hit!"

6. In what type of establishment was *Cheers* set?

7. The Dandie Dinmont terrier is named after a character in which novel?

8. Larissa is a moon of which planet?

9. What game does the Queen of Hearts order Alice to play in *Alice in Wonderland*?

10. Which flower was Monet most famous for painting?

11. What's the female version of a Bar Mitzvah?

12. What country was called Northern Rhodesia until 1984?

13. What is a vardo?

14. Who wrote *War and Peace*?

15. In which cartoon would you find the character Peppermint Patty?

16. Who was Toronto's crack-smoking mayor?

17. In Greek Myth, what was the food of the Gods?

18. Which European country ruled Macau until December 20th 1999?

19. Who was charged with the murder of Robert Kennedy?

20. What number does Lionel Messi wear?

Bits and Pieces 5

1. What is the name of the main railway station in Glasgow?

2. The Swiss town of Locarno is located at the northern end of which lake?

3. What name is given to the day before Good Friday?

4. Who invented condensed milk in 1856?

5. Who was charged with the murder of the Lindbergh Baby?

6. What name is given to a container for cigars?

7. Who was the judge most associated with the O.J. Simpson trial?

8. What is the most populous US State?

9. How many children did *Roseanne* have?

10. Where is the most northerly racecourse in the UK?

11. Who wrote *The Girl on the Train*?

12. What is Lipton the world's biggest-selling brand of?

13. Who wrote *A Christmas Carol*?

14. Where is Lake Como?

15. What is the Paris Gare Du Nord?

16. Of what is the ohm the standard measurement?

17. By what nickname was Simon Bolivar also known?

18. Who wrote the song *Blue Moon*?

19. What is the chief town of Jersey?

20. Where in Gretna Green is the most popular place to be married?

"Throwers and Knowers"

Bits and Pieces 6

1. What is it called when a baby is born bottom first instead of head first?

2. Which New England state doesn't border the Atlantic Ocean?

3. Who 'couldn't see a belt without hitting below it'?

4. Who is the baddy in the Disney film *Aladdin*?

5. Who pulls the Sovereigns coffin at a Royal funeral?

6. What city has won the Britain in Bloom competition a record-breaking ten times?

7. What is the name of the Headquarters of the Metropolitan Police?

"You've had a good night out - but you go home with nowt!"

8. What does a hygrometer measure?

9. Who presented *Newsnight* for 25 years?

10. What is a Browning M2?

11. What L is sometimes used to refer to the mainly Spanish speaking areas of the Americas?

12. Who gave a V sign to the judges at the British Show Jumping Derby?

13. In computers, how many nibbles are in a byte?

14. Captain James Cook discovered what country in 1769 and claimed it for Great Britain?

15. At what temperature would both a Fahrenheit and Celsius thermometer show a reading of the same number?

16. What was the Welsh version of *Geordie Shore*?

17. In what year was Queen Elizabeth II born?

18. What is the least populous American state?

19. What colour is associated with The Labour Party?

20. Who was the lead singer of The Supremes?

Bits and Pieces 7

1. What was the name of the Netflix series examining the trial of Steven Avery?

2. What was the name of the three-headed dog that guarded the gates to Hades?

3. Who is Kermit's girlfriend?

4. In what country will you find 'The Blue Lagoon' spa?

5. What name is given to the part of a beach which lies between low and high tide?

6. In what year did Pac-Man make its US debut?

7. Who voices Elsa in *Frozen*?

"Throwers and Knowers"

8. What is the name of the main railway station in Edinburgh?

9. What Nobel Prize-winning author committed suicide by gunshot in 1961?

10. What was the name of Long John Silver's parrot?

11. What is a yurt?

12. Who resigned as presenter of *The One Show* in 2010?

13. What movie helped popularize disco music worldwide?

14. Who was tried and acquitted for the 1892 axe murders of her father and her stepmother?

15. Who created *Spider-Man*, *The Hulk*, *The Fantastic Four*, *Iron Man*, *Thor* and the *X-Men*?

16. What is Craps?

17. What was the name of Bernie Winters' dog?

18. To what island group does Corfu belong?

19. In which film did the fictional company of WC Boggs appear?

20. In what book did Rudyard Kipling introduce readers to a mongoose named Rikki Tikki Tavi?

Bits and Pieces 8

1. What is the largest town in Dorset?

2. Who played General Patton in *Patton*?

3. Who led the Yorkshire Ripper enquiry?

4. Which duo starred in *Up in Smoke*?

5. Whose biggest hit was *He's On The Phone*?

6. In what year was Thomas Becket murdered?

7. In what year was the Guinness Brewery founded?

8. What is the county town of Cumbria?

9. Who played Roseanne's sister in *Roseanne*?

10. What was Jackson Pollock's nickname?

11. What T is a tax on exports and imports?

12. What is the main constituent of the air we breathe?

13. What name is given to the perceived decrease in air temperature felt by the body on exposed skin due to the flow of air?

14. If you are 'called to the bar', what profession are you in?

15. What singer appeared in the first live television broadcast in the UK?

16. In what year did Gloria Gaynor have a number one hit with *I Will Survive*?

17. Who painted the Sistine Chapel ceiling?

18. What ancient Roman festival that begins on 17th December had some of its customs absorbed into Christmas?

19. Who was the only member of the Lord of the Rings cast or crew who actually met J.R.R. Tolkien?

20. In which city is *The Phantom of the Opera* set?

"Now the cash you won for charity earlier... that's safe."

Bits and Pieces 9

1. What is a London plane?

2. Who played Butch in *Pulp Fiction*?

3. What L is a byword for Satan?

4. Of which organization was Lord Reith founder?

5. What year was the Amazon Kindle Fire first introduced?

6. How many of the seven dwarves have beards?

7. What organization was given the only Nobel peace prize awarded during World War I?

8. How is the Central Criminal Court of England better known?

9. In which county is Blackpool located?

10. What film was based on the novel *Heart of Darkness*?

11. Who did John Goodman play in *Roseanne*?

12. Bertie Wooster and Flashman are both residents of what London Square?

13. Who wrote *The Lost World*?

14. Who directed *Edward Scissorhands*?

15. In which Belgian town is Stella Artois brewed?

16. In 1915, what steamship was torpedoed by a German submarine, killing over 1000 passengers?

17. What church near the town of Portadown, Northern Ireland has become a hotspot in marching season?

18. What chocolate bar was 'full of Eastern promise'?

19. What salty, meaty drink is made in Burton on Trent?

20. Which two friends won Oscars for their screenplay of the 1997 movie *Good Will Hunting*?

"Stay out of the black and into the red, nothing in this game for two in a bed."

Bits and Pieces 10

1. How did Jackson Pollock die?

2. Who wrote *Moby Dick*?

3. What is the largest city in North Carolina?

4. Who was the country of Rhodesia named after?

5. Who has hosted the Academy Awards more than any other host?

6. Who appeared in five films during six years that were nominated for the Academy Award for Best Picture?

7. Which chemical element has the atomic number 2?

8. What two modern day countries comprise the Iberian Peninsula?

9. What would you add to lager to make it a lager tops?

10. In which English county is Canvey Island situated?

11. What is Cosplay?

12. What is the line most used in movies?

13. What Japanese word for 'wave person' refers to a masterless samurai?

14. What is the French word for motorway?

15. What is the usual colour of copper sulphate?

16. Who wrote *The Prince*?

17. What name was given to the wooden frame used for hanging?

18. What flower is the symbol of England?

19. What cooking fuel is produced by heating wood without oxygen?

20. What famous clipper ship took its name from a Scots words for a short shirt in a Robert Burns poem?

"Look at what you could have won."

Bits and Pieces 11

1. Which of the Seven Dwarves does not have a beard?

2. What do Dacia make?

3. How did Natasha Richardson die?

4. Where was 'New Sweden'?

"And Bully's Special Priiiiize..."

5. In what city would you find Zavantem Airport?

6. How many years were between the Wright brothers' first successful flight and the first time we landed on the moon?

7. What film gave us the first time Warner Brothers and Disney characters appeared together on screen?

8. Who was the BBC's Royal Correspondent during the 90s?

9. What was the first US city to have a subway system?

10. How are the negative particles in an atom known?

11. Who said to whom, 'You have been in Afghanistan, I perceive'?

12. Which oil rig exploded on 6th July 1988?

13. What battle was a 'close run thing'?

14. What country was called the Gold Coast prior to its 1957 independence?

15. Who sang *Night Fever*?

16. What name was given to the Muslim inhabitants of the Iberian peninsula?

17. What was named for Pope Sixtus IV when it was consecrated in a 1483 Mass?

18. What year was the novel *War & Peace* first published in its entirety?

19. Which U.S. President ended his country's participation in the Vietnam War?

20. Which English football club has won the European Cup 5 times?

Bits and Pieces 12

1. Which is the largest country in Africa by area?

2. Who is the Patron Saint of Scotland?

3. Which thespian character is played by Matt Berry?

4. You might sign off a letter with TTFN. What does TTFN stand for?

5. Which TV presenter was in a relationship with James Middleton, brother of Kate Middleton?

6. What quiz was founded by John P. Gwynn?

7. What was General Patton's nickname?

8. Which road runs from London to Fishguard in Wales?

9. Who has been the second most-translated author in the world since 1979?

10. In what year was Princess Diana born?

"Now the cash you won for charity earlier... that's safe."

11. Which chemical element is represented by the letter N?

12. What name is given to a young cat?

13. What character name connects *Men Behaving Badly* and *The Wizard of Oz*?

14. Who played Lawrence in the movie *Lawrence of Arabia*?

15. Who famously petitioned the US Congress for the National Park bill?

16. Who was Denis Goodwin's comedy partner?

17. What was stolen on Christmas Day 1950?

18. In which country was Gandhi born?

19. Which Prime Minister was born on 9th July 1916?

20. Who directed the film of Ken Kesey's novel *One Flew Over The Cuckoo's Nest*?

Bits and Pieces 13

1. What Latin expression means "an act or event that provokes or is used to justify war"?

2. What was the last film directed by Stanley Kubrick?

3. What is an apiarist?

4. Who was Queen Elizabeth II's younger sister?

5. Roy Carroll played in goals for Northern Ireland in 2016, in what year did he win his first cap?

6. In South Africa, who was 'Uncle Paul'?

7. On what island was the Duke of Edinburgh born?

8. What is the name of ABBA's debut album?

9. Where are the headquarters of the Nationwide Building Society?

10. What was Mozart's christian name?

11. Which is colder, the North or South Pole?

12. What is the largest building society in the world?

13. Who was burned at the stake on 30th May 1431?

14. Who directed *The Devils*?

15. Where will you find Mahe?

16. What is a pike?

17. What type of animal was 'Jaws'?

18. Who was the youngest member of the Jackson 5?

19. What substance are fingernails made of?

20. Who is the city of Monrovia named after?

"Super, smashing, great."

Bits and Pieces 14

1. Which company gave us 'Candy Crush'?

2. What was the name of the Crusade sent to destroy The Cathars?

3. How many people died in the Piper Alpha disaster?

4. What are the only two consecutive prime numbers?

5. How is David John White better known?

6. What are you afraid of if you have 'chionophobia'?

7. How are The Yeomen Warders better known?

8. Who is Angelina Jolie's father?

9. What nationality is journalist Lyse Doucet?

10. In what town did the 'De Feo' murders occur?

"Innnnnn one..."

11. The name of what city of the United Kingdom means 'mouth of the sandbars'?

12. What was the first *Harry Potter* film? *the Philosopher's stone*

13. Who administered Syria after WWI?

14. Which significant Bedfordshire town lies halfway between Luton and Milton Keynes?

15. What blog is 'the source for daily Manhattan media news and gossip'

16. What was the most common car to be found in East Germany?

17. What did Rhodesia become?

18. What is a second full moon in a month called?

19. Who was *The Noble Yachtsman*?

20. Who wrote the *Uncle Remus* stories?

Bits and Pieces 15

1. What instrument is associated with Jacqueline du Pré?

2. Wearside Jack was a hoaxer during which investigation?

3. How many legs does an octopus have?

4. Leonardo da Vinci's *Madonna of the Yarnwinder* was stolen from which Scottish castle in 2003?

5. What station is the Central London terminus for South West Trains?

6. What was stolen on 21st August 1911?

7. When George Bush asked us to read his lips, what were the next 3 words?

8. What is the name of the drink made from fermented honey?

9. Who was Bruce Wayne's butler?

10. What is the name of the main railway station in Bristol?

11. Which literary work's title character is named Edmond Dantes?

12. Who is best known for his painting *American Gothic*?

13. Where was St Paul born?

14. Who wrote *Alice's Adventures in Wonderland*?

15. What is the longest canal in Britain?

16. What can a polyglot do?

17. Of which Scottish city is Prince Philip the Duke?

18. What name is given to the study of Chinese topics?

19. To what is the University of Paris usually referred?

20. Who wrote *Brief Encounter*?

"You win nothing but your BFH... Bus Fare Home"

Bits and Pieces 16

1. Who founded Selfridge's Department Store?

2. Turin is the capital of which area of Italy?

3. What name was given to attempts to turn base metals into gold?

4. What Welshman won BBC Sports Personality of the Year in 1960?

5. What kind of animal is a sidewinder?

6. Who is the Patron Saint of Hopeless Causes?

7. Who wrote *The New Machiavelli*?

8. Who narrated more episodes of the BBC children's TV series *Jackanory* than anyone else?

9. Which English county has the longest coastline?

10. In Disney's *The Little Mermaid*, what is the main character's name?

"101 or more with 6 darts for tonight's mystery star prize"

11. Which steam locomotive was the first to hit 100mph in the UK?

12. What club have been in the English top flight for the longest period?

13. Who became the first American to orbit the Earth?

14. Who was the only cast member to appear in all 128 episodes of *Dawson's Creek*?

15. What is the third largest city in the UK?

16. Which island of Japan is just 26 miles form Russia at its closest point?

17. What tropic passes through Australia?

18. What is the main export of Botswana?

19. What began in America on January 24th 1848?

20. Who was the oldest member of The BeeGees?

Bits and Pieces 17

1. In which country was Mel Gibson born?

2. In which country did the My Lai massacre take place?

3. What do Americans call *Cluedo*?

4. What dance studios were founded by Debbie Moore?

5. In what year was chip and pin rolled out nationally in the UK?

6. What kind of ship was The Cutty Sark?

7. In which county will you find the village of Darfield?

8. What was Beethoven's christian name?

9. Who was the oldest goalscorer in World Cup history?

10. Which lemon and lime drink was launched at around the same time as the 1929 Wall Street Crash?

11. What is traditionally recognized as the smallest English county?

12. What colour jersey does the overall leader of the Tour de France wear?

13. What future celebrity made an appearance as Danny in *City Slickers*?

14. How many sides on a hexagon?

15. In which city is Byker an area?

16. As of 2016, has Jake Gyllenhaal ever won an Oscar?

17. Who takes a wry look at TV in the show *Screenwipe*?

18. The first live television broadcast in the UK took place in what Essex town?

19. What was the name of Winston Churchill's wife?

20. What river runs through Braintree?

"All for the throw of a dart"

Bits and Pieces 18

1. What is Ace Ventura's occupation?

2. Who was the first Westerner to travel to the central portion of the Niger River?

3. Which explorer from Blantyre, Scotland was a hero of the Victorian age?

4. In what year was the Channel Tunnel opened?

5. Where is William Rufus buried?

6. Who connects the rules of Boxing to the downfall of Oscar Wilde?

7. In what year was the destruction of Pompeii by the eruption of Vesuvius?

"Go for your lights"

8. What treaty of 1898 saw Spain relinquish virtually all of their Empire?

9. In what year did the Roman Conquest of Britain begin?

10. Which man, born in 1868, has been referred to as 'the greatest British architect'?

11. Who was the husband of Queen Nefertiti?

12. In what year did The Slave Trade Act become law, abolishing the slave trade in the British Empire?

13. Who ruled England from 1653 to 1658?

14. In what year did the Berlin Wall come down?

15. Which historical figure is portrayed in more films than any other?

16. On which island did Napoleon die?

17. Where in London was Rod Stewart born?

18. What was Lady Gaga's first UK No. 1?

19. Who asked us to *Tell Laura I Love Her*?

20. Who sang *Try A Little Tenderness* in 1966?

Bits and Pieces 19

1. Who sang *Bette Davis Eyes*?

2. How many people were in The Thompson Twins when they had their biggest success?

3. The kids from which TV show gave us the pop hit *Just Say No!*?

4. Who had a hit in 1989 with *We Didn't Start the Fire*?

5. Which singer had more weeks in the UK chart than any other in the 1980s?

6. Which band included Jeff Lynne, Roy Orbison and Tom Petty?

7. Whose first UK hit was *Nothing Can Divide Us*?

8. What was Joshua Kadison's biggest hit?

9. Who was known as Sporty Spice?

10. Who had a number one with *Cotton Eyed Joe*?

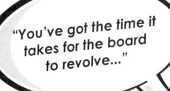

"You've got the time it takes for the board to revolve..."

11. Who were Ready to Go?

12. Which London Theatre suffered a roof collapse in 2013?

13. What street is considered the centre of London's West End Theatre District?

14. What famous painting can be found in church of Santa Maria delle Grazie, Milan?

15. What is Shakespeare's shortest play?

16. Which art movement began in Zurich in 1916?

17. Whose most famous surviving work is the Garden of Earthly Delights?

18. Rodin is best remembered for his work in what field?

19. Which famous prize is given each year to a British visual artist under the age of 50?

20. Which gallery is housed in the former Bankside Power Station?

Bits and Pieces 20

1. What name is given to the period of Italian Culture, between the 14th and 17th C, which is often said to be the bridge between the Middle Ages and Modern History?

2. Which modern artist caused controversy with his preserved shark artwork?

3. Which architect designed the Glasgow School of Art?

4. Where would you find the Louvre?

5. Who created the Daleks?

6. Who presented *Catchphrase* from 1986 to 1999?

"Look at what you could have won."

7. What international gameshow introduced us to the big red balls?

8. Which long-running gameshow is based on *Noughts and Crosses*?

9. Who hosted *15 to 1* for many years?

10. Which British show was originally intended to be a remake of France's *Fort Boyard*?

11. What Native American leader surrendered at Skeleton Canyon in 1886?

12. In which state was Stephen King born?

13. Which state is 'The Show Me' state?

14. Which US state is nicknamed the Palmetto State?

15. What is the only US state whose entire northern border is formed by a river?

16. In which American city was *Cheers* set?

17. What was the original name of the Statue of Liberty?

18. Which of the Presidents on Mt Rushmore is wearing glasses?

19. What is the capital of the state of Nevada?

20. What is the most populous city of the USA?

Book First Lines

1. 'It is a truth universally acknowledged, that a single man in possession of a good fortune, must be in want of a wife' is the first line of which book?

2. 'In my younger and more vulnerable years my father gave me some advice that I've been turning over in my mind ever since'?

3. Which book begins, 'Call me Ishmael'?

4. Which four children are named in the first line of *The Lion, The Witch and The Wardrobe*?

5. What book begins, 'My father and mother should have stayed in New York where they met and married and where I was born'?

"You can't beat a bit of Bully!"

6. Which book starts with, 'Hale knew, before he had been in Brighton three hours, that they meant to murder him'?

7. 'It was a bright cold day in April and the clocks were striking thirteen'?

8. What book begins,'In the week before their departure to Arrakis, when all the final scurrying about had reached a nearly unbearable frenzy, an old crone came to visit the mother of the boy, Paul.'?

9. 'Whether I shall turn out to be the hero of my own life, or whether that station will be held by anybody else, these pages must show'?

10. What book begins, 'To the red country and part of the gray country of Oklahoma, the last rains came gently, and they did not cut the scarred earth'?

11. What book begins, 'When he was nearly thirteen, my brother Jem got his arm badly broken at the elbow'?

12. Which Dickens character is mentioned in the first line of *Catcher in the Rye*?

13. Which Dr Seuss book begins 'The sun did not shine, it was too wet to play, so we sat in the house all that cold, cold wet day'?

14. What book begins, 'Robert Langdon awoke slowly'?

15. 'All children, except one, grow up', is the first line of which book?

16. What book begins, 'Alice was beginning to get very tired of sitting by her sister on the bank'?

17. What book begins, 'Left Munich at 8.35 p.m. on 1st May, arriving at Vienna early next morning; should have arrived at 6.46, but train was an hour late'?

18. The night was sultry is the opening line of a book around which 1980s film pivots?

19. What is the first line of *A Tale of Two Cities*?

20. Which book starts with 'Christmas won't be Christmas without any presents,' grumbled Jo, lying on the rug?

Books 1

1 What Robert Louis Stevenson novel was originally published under the title *The Sea-Cook*?

2 Who is best known for writing *The Chronicles of Narnia*?

3 Who wrote the novel, *The Shining*?

4 Who wrote *Stardust*?

5 Which Professor is a recurring character in most Dan Brown books?

6 Who wrote *The Hunchback of Notre Dame*?

7 Who has been the most-translated author in the world since 1979?

8 Whose autobiography was, *Still Got It, Never Lost It!*?

9 Which book is subtitled *The Children's Crusade*?

10 Whose first book was *The Mysterious Affair at Styles*?

11 What genre would you associate with HP Lovecraft?

12 Whose autobiography was called, *The Good, The Bad and Me*?

13 What is the name of Sherlock Holmes' arch-enemy?

14 Who wrote *Tom Jones*?

15 Whose autobiography was called *Just One More Thing*?

16 Who wrote *Wuthering Heights*?

17 Who is credited with writing the first detective story, *The Murders in the Rue Morgue*?

18 Whose autobiography was entitled *Time to say Hello*?

19 Where is *Trainspotting* set?

20 Who gave us *Don't Hassle the Hoff*?

"Remember, you can't beat a bit of Bully!"

Books 2

1. Who gave us *Riders*?

2. Whose autobiography was called *Lips Unsealed*?

3. Who wrote *The Martian*?

4. Johanna Basford was behind some of the bestselling books of 2015, what were they?

5. Who wrote *Around the World in 80 Days*?

6. Whose autobiography was entitled *The Bedwetter*?

7. Who penned a famous memoir called *The Moon's A Balloon*?

8. Whose autobiography was called *I'm a Believer*?

9. What books are the most famous creations of Suzanne Collins?

10. Who was Don Quixote's sidekick?

11. In the Roald Dahl book, who is The Champion of the World?

12. In *50 Shades of Grey*, who does Christian Grey desire?

13. Which is the only Dickens novel with a female narrator?

14. Who was *Born Standing Up*?

15. Which book is subtitled *The Saga of an American Family*?

16. Which Phillip K Dick book looks at an alternative reality where the USA is split between German and Japanese empires?

17. Whose autobiography was called *The Audacity of Hope*?

18. Who wrote the original James Bond books?

19. Who wrote *The Godfather*?

20. Which book begins, 'Happy families are all alike; every unhappy family is unhappy in its own way'?

"Bully's bellowed you out there!"

Books 3

1. Who wrote *The Jungle Book*?

2. Whose autobiography was called *The Elephant to Hollywood*?

3. Which novel is set in the Marcia Blaine School for Girls in Edinburgh?

4. Who wrote the *Harry Potter* stories?

5. What is Mr Pickwick's first name in *The Pickwick Papers*?

6. The Emerald City is the capital of which fictional land?

7. Who wrote Tom Brown's *Schooldays*?

8. Whose autobiography was called Stori Telling?

9. Who wrote *Fifty Shades of Grey*?

10. What was Harry Potter's father's name?

11. What is Jack Dawkins' nickname in Oliver Twist?

12. Who wrote Billy Budd, Sailor?

13. What was Phillip K Dick's middle name?

14. Whose autobiography was called Mein Kampf?

15. Who created Tarzan?

16. Who is the main character in Ulysses?

17. The Curse of Capistrano, a 1919 story by Johnston McCulley, is the first work to feature which fictional character?

18. Who wrote Anne of Green Gables?

19. What is Frances Hodgson Burnett's most famous book?

20. Who was telling the truth when he wrote It's Not About The Bike?

"101 or more with 6 darts for tonight's mystery star prize"

Books 4

1. Who created the character *Don Quixote*?

2. Who wrote *The Satanic Verses*?

3. Who wrote *Jurassic Park* and *Congo*?

4. In what year was *The Da Vinci Code* first published?

5. Who wrote *Heart of Darkness*?

"Let's check that with Bully"

6. Who wrote the *Lovejoy* stories?

7. Whose unbelievably true life story was entitled *Total Recall*?

8. Whose autobiography was called *The Sport of Queens*?

9. In which year was the first *Harry Potter* book released?

10. Which Eastenders star's autobiography was called *Rags to Ritchie*?

11. In *Alice in Wonderland*, who did Alice follow down the tunnel?

12. Who wrote *Cold Comfort Farm*?

13. Who was *Losing My Virginity*?

14. What year was the first *Twilight* novel published?

15. Who wrote *The Tiger Who Came to Tea*?

16. Who was Harper Lee married to?

17. What character is Robert E. Howard's most famous creation?

18. Whose autobiography was called *My Word Is My Bond*?

19. In Jonathan Swift's *Gulliver's Travels*, what was Gulliver's first name?

20. Who wrote the original *Winnie the Pooh* stories?

Brilliant Bills

"The subjects that are lit are the ones you can hit!"

1. Billy Shears was whose alter ego?

2. What was the real name of Buffalo Bill?

3. Which Bill is the richest man in the world as of 2015?

4. Which Bill is a comedian who went on the *Part Troll* tour?

5. Buffalo Bill was the serial killer in *The Silence of the Lambs*, who played Buffalo Bill in the 1991 movie?

6. Bilbo Baggins is the title character of what book?

7. Which Bill is the comic host of American show *Real Time*?

8. Which Bill was a member of *The Goodies*?

9. Which Bill was TV's 'Compo'?

10. Which Bill appeared in a couple of *Carry On* films and many series of *Heartbeat*?

11. Which Bill was the producer of Musical *Blood Brothers*?

12. Which Bill was the star of *Caddyshack* and *Scrooged*?

13. Which Bill had the middle name Jefferson and plays the saxophone?

14. Which Bill directed *Gregory's Girl*?

15. Which Bill was a controversial US comedian who died at age 32?

16. Which Bill made Rock and Roll popular?

17. Which Bill led England to their first Grand Slam in 23 years?

18. Which Bill is one of the world's biggest selling travel writers?

19. If you are 'a friend of Bill', what organisation are you probably a member of?

20. Which Bill starred in *Twister* and *Titanic*?

Business 1

1. At which store would you collect Clubcard points?

2. How do we usually refer to a loan secured against property?

3. What food company is listed on the New York Stock Exchange with the single letter K?

4. Which 479 strong supermarket chain was bought by Morrisons in 2004?

5. Who was the founder of Tesco?

6. What company was founded by Richard Block & David Quayle ?

7. Where was the first ever Kwik Save supermarket opened?

8. Who founded Microsoft and is now one of the world's richest men?

9. What service is offered by William Hill and Coral?

10. What famous bike company is associated with Nottingham?

11. In what city was the company Xerox formed?

"Let's check that with Bully"

12. What does LIBOR stand for?

13. In which country is Samsung based?

14. Whose unauthorised trading caused the demise of Barings Bank?

15. Which Canadian lingerie firm operates around 60 stores in the UK?

16. Richard Wall founded a company in the 1780s that is still well known. What does the company make?

17. Which company launched the first credit card outside of the US?

18. Which British Businessman is famous for his 'Cabaret of Angels'?

19. What was the first product in human history which sold over 1,000,000 units?

20. Who was the biggest UK retailer by sales (as of 2014)?

Business 2

1. Which UK retailer shares its name with a city in Greece?

2. Which UK retailer was founded in Worksop in 1930?

3. Which high street retailer, focusing on frozen foods, is based in north Wales?

4. The name of which high street store became a slang term for 'mental'?

5. Which famous high street retailer was founded in Leeds in 1884?

6. What computer company is often referred to as HP?

7. Which company produces Hellmann's mayonnaise and Dove shampoo?

8. 'A better life, a better world', is a slogan associated with which company?

9. Where is it believed that the first cheque for one million pounds was written?

10. From which country did the company IKEA originate?

11. What industry was Stewarts & Lloyds involved in?

12. What do Whittard of Chelsea sell?

13. J. Arthur Rank's father made his fortune in what business?

14. What is the name of the largest French retailer?

15. The French word *Bourse* usually refers to what?

16. What do Michelin make?

17. In what year did the last Woolworths stores close in the UK?

18. Which Scottish businesswoman has been dubbed Baroness Bra?

19. Who founded Facebook?

20. Who is the CEO of Apple as of early 2016?

"You've had a good night out - but you go home with nowt!"

Capital Cities

1. What is the most northerly capital city in the world?

2. What city is the capital of Germany?

3. What is the capital city of The Dominican Republic?

4. What is the capital of Cyprus?

5. What is the capital of Serbia?

6. What is the capital of Kosovo?

7. What is the capital of Puerto Rico?

"Throwers and Knowers"

8. What is the capital city of Venezuela?

9. What is the capital city of New Zealand?

10. What is the capital city of Ukraine?

11. What is the capital city of Panama?

12. What is the capital city of South Sudan?

13. What is the capital city of Nepal?

14. What is the capital city of Bangladesh?

15. What is the capital of Liberia?

16. What city is the capital of Japan?

17. What is the capital city of Ireland?

18. Which city is the capital of India?

19. What is the capital of Botswana?

20. Banjul is the capital of what country?

Catchphrases

1. Which cartoon character had the catchphrase 'What's up Doc?'

2. Ooh, Betty!' was a favourite catchphrase of the 70s. Which character is it associated with?

3. Which sitcom would you associate the catchphrase 'Don't panic!'?

4. Which comedy character is associated with the catchphrase 'Aha!'?

5. Who would say 'You'll like this, not a lot'?

6. Which Prime Minister promised to 'be tough on crime, tough on the causes of crime'?

7. Whose catchphrase was 'You dirty ol' man'?

8. In what show did Dale Winton have the catchphrase 'Bring back your partners!'?

9. What was Leslie Crowther's catchphrase on *The Price is Right*?

10. Whose catchphrase was 'Is it cos I is black'?

"Now the cash you won for charity earlier... that's safe."

11. What catchphrase is most associated with the show *Hawaii Five-0*?

12. Which Clint Eastwood character had the catchphrase, 'Go ahead, make my day'?

13. Whose catchphrase was 'How tickled I am!'?

14. 'I don't believe it!' is the catchphrase of which comedy character?

15. Who first used the catchphrase, 'if it's up there I'll give you the money myself'?

16. Whose catchphrase was 'turned out nice again'?

17. What is Homer Simpson's catchphrase?

18. Whose catchphrase was 'Cheap as chips'?

19. Which TV baddy would say 'Exterminate'?

20. 'Spoon, jar, jar, spoon' was whose catchphrase?

Comedy

1. In which town was *The Good Life* set?

2. What was the name of the Department store in *Are You Being Served*?

3. What show links Ulrika Jonsson and Will Self?

4. What was the name of Ricky Gervais' character in *The Office*?

5. What Peter Kay character was a parody of the generic talent show winner?

6. How is Allan Konigsberg better known?

7. What popular comedian wrote a book titled *I Am America (And So Can You!)*?

8. Who was Ronnie Corbett's long term comedy partner?

9. Which Irish comedian is the narrator on *Ex On The Beach*?

10. Which *Father Ted* writer went on to pen *The IT Crowd*?

11. What was the name of the teacher played by John Alderton in *Please Sir!*?

12. What was Raymond's occupation in *Everybody Loves Raymond*?

13. What sitcom was a spin-off from *Cheers*?

14. Who did Tom Bosley play in *Happy Days*?

15. Who played Betty in *Some Mothers Do 'Ave 'Em*?

16. Royston Vasey, the fictitious town in *The League of Gentlemen*, is actually the real name of which comedian?

17. What is Vic Reeves' real name?

18. What 80s comedy character was played by Matt Frewer?

19. What was the name of the spin-off series to *On the Buses*?

20. Which duo gave us the famous *Four Candles* sketch?

"Super, smashing, great."

Curious Questions 1

1. What are the 3 main sub-atomic particles?

2. What term is used to describe the region straddling the upper Northeastern United States, the Great Lakes, and the Midwest States, referring to economic decline, population loss, and urban decay?

3. What are the Christian names of *The Hardy Boys*?

4. On which planet does He-Man live?

5. How many possible first moves are there in chess?

6. Who was appointed Manager of Valencia in December 2015?

7. Who played the title character in *Bugsy Malone*?

8. Which company took over 99p Stores in 2015?

9. Which controversial TV personality said 'Little sweaty jocks, sending us Ebola bombs in the form of sweaty Glaswegians just isn't cricket. Scottish NHS sucks'?

10. Who is the villain in *101 Dalmatians*?

11. St. Louis' Gateway Arch is officially named for what US president?

12. What is a group of Pandas called?

13. What band was Lisa Lopes a member of?

14. What record label was formed by Paul Morley and Trevor Horn?

15. What was Muse's biggest UK hit?

16. Who is Bruce Wayne's butler?

17. Where is the smallest racecourse in the UK?

18. Who was the first female president of the Academy of Motion Picture Arts and Sciences?

19. Who is Patty Smyth married to?

20. In the nursery rhyme, who grew whiskers on his chin again?

"Innnnnn two..."

Curious Questions 2

1. Who wrote *Dreams From My Father*?

2. What is the use of living systems and organisms to develop or make products?

3. In Scotland, what type of flower is a campanula rotundifolia?

4. With whom did Mel B record I Want You Back?

5. Bolton lies 10 miles North West of what city?

6. What is the Cenotaph made from?

7. Who pioneered the backwards jump in the high jump?

8. What instrument was Acker Bilk famed for playing?

9. In what city was Eddie Murphy born?

10. What type of cloud can form a tornado?

11. According to the song, which gift was given on the Fifth day of Christmas?

12. From what country does the character of Borat come from?

13. What happened to Solomon Grundy on Wednesday?

14. Where is Ted Stevens Airport?

15. What is Shakespeare's longest play?

16. What did the 'Hollywood' sign say before it said Hollywood?

17. Which Nigel was a judge on So You Think You Can Dance?

18. In what city are Twitter's headquarters?

19. A Copper is a nickname for what occupation?

20. Signs around which US beach city proclaim '27 miles of scenic beauty'?

"You win nothing but your BFH... Bus Fare Home"

Curious Questions 3

1. What was the name of John Savident's character in *Coronation Street*?

2. In which city can the Harley-Davidson Museum be found?

3. What company makes IRN-BRU?

4. What name is given to a special kind of umbrella used to protect you from sunlight?

5. Which Welsh abbey was founded by Walter de Clare, Lord of Chepstow, on 9th May 1131?

6. Complete the Joke: 'How do you kill a Circus'?

7. What does BAFTA stand for?

8. Three of Ginger Rogers' five husbands had the same name, what was it?

9. What is Paul McKenna famous for?

"101 or more with 6 darts for tonight's mystery star prize"

10. When was the first San Diego Comic-Con International?

11. Who produced *Howard the Duck*?

12. Which character was the jack-in-the-box in *The Magic Roundabout*?

13. Which international news agency is headquartered in Canary Wharf?

14. What nationality was Kofi Annan?

15. Mount Rushmore is located near which town in South Dakota?

16. 'Ye cannae shove yer granny off a bus' is a variation of what children's song?

17. Who led America to victory in the Spanish-American War?

18. In what organ of the human body would you find the endometrium?

19. What was the name given to the group who sought to purify the Church of England from all Roman Catholic practices?

20. Which duo gave us *The Flintstones*, *The Jetsons* and *Yogi Bear* amongst others?

Curious Questions 4

1. In what year was Lady Gaga born?

2. At school, what does GCSE stand for?

3. Where is NATO headquartered?

4. What is Elton John's middle name?

"All for the throw of a dart"

5. HBO's TV show *True Blood* is based on a book series by whom?

6. What cheese is made backwards?

7. What was Frank Sinatra's middle name?

8. Who was given a gift of a hat pin and a copy of Leaves of Grass on February 28th 1997?

9. Which character killed Uncle Tom?

10. What name is given to the contrivance of a false appearance of virtue or goodness, while concealing real character or inclination?

11. Who is the youngest person ever to win a competitive Academy Award?

12. What is Sean Connery's real christian name?

13. In the UK, what prize is for excellence in architecture each year?

14. Who went from *Clash of the Titans* to *LA Law*?

15. How did Virginia Woolf die?

16. In which Scottish region is the village of Gretna?

17. What is the study of heredity referred to as?

18. How are Walkers crisps known in the USA?

19. Who was a key member of The Spencer Davis Group, Traffic, Blind Faith and Go?

20. What do we call the day after Christmas?

Curious Questions 5

1. In what year did the Soviet Union release the last of their German WW2 POWs?

2. Who wrote *Ulysses*?

3. Who succeeded Kofi Annan as Secretary General of the United Nations?

4. Who led UKIP in the 2015 General Election?

5. Where is the biggest Power Station in Britain?

6. Bronze is an alloy of what two metals?

7. Who was the oldest Spice Girl?

8. What city was Anton Cermak killed in?

9. What was the name of the Spice Girl's debut album?

10. What is the nickname of the state of Pennsylvania?

"Go for your lights"

11. Who was Al Gore's running mate in the 2000 US General Election?

12. What seat is held by Iain Duncan Smith?

13. Who had a hit with *Lust for Life*?

14. What nickname is often given to Warren Buffett?

15. Which country does Shakira come from?

16. Which King began the building of the Palace of Versailles?

17. A text is sometimes referred to as an SMS. What does SMS stand for?

18. What is Dido's real name?

19. What was the first geological period of the Paleozoic Era?

20. What name was given to the group of actors including Rex Harrison, Boris Karloff, Stan Laurel, Basil Rathbone, Ronald Colman and Leslie Howard?

Curious Questions 6

1. What children's books character lives in the Hundred Acre Woods?

2. In which city did Ayrton Senna die?

3. What is the umbrella term for the Special Forces in Russia?

4. In whose flat did Mama Cass die?

5. On what island did the dodo live?

6. What do you call a group of alpacas?

7. What was the name of the last deep coal mine in Scotland?

8. Who was Ronald Reagan's first wife?

9. In which town would you find the Octagon Theatre?

10. What name is given to the stones in a bird's stomach, used to grind food?

11. If a plant is perennial, how long does it live?

12. How many players in a Rugby League team?

13. Which general's father led the investigation of the Lindbergh baby kidnapping?

14. What book does each girl receive as a Christmas present at the start of *Little Women*?

15. Who sang *Who's Sorry Now* in 1958?

16. In what country would you find the active volcano Santorini?

17. In what year did Al Jolson die?

18. What trench is the deepest part of the world's oceans?

19. In the field of medicine, what does MRI stand for?

20. Who created *The Twilight Zone*?

"You've got the time it takes for the board to revolve..."

Curious Questions 7

1. What UK racecourse is known as The Roodee?

2. Complete the Joke: 'A bar of gold walks into a bar. The barman says…'?

3. In the army, what does MP stand for?

4. Who produced the 80s smash *Relax*?

5. What did the L stand for in the name of author L. Frank Baum?

6. What branch of medicine deals with the study and treatment of cancer?

7. In March 2010, what serious accident was Stirling Moss involved in?

8. What interesting crossing of the Tyne was opened in 2001?

9. What is believed to be the top e-commerce website in the world?

10. The majority of the world's real cinnamon comes from what island nation?

"Up to the oche - and listen to Tony!"

11. Where was Amir Khan born?

12. What was the name of Tom Jones' wife?

13. What is daltonism?

14. Which cartoon characters might you encounter in *Equestria*?

15. What is the nickname of Bolton Wanderers FC?

16. How many fingers does a boy scout extend in a salute?

17. In what year did Richard Burton die?

18. Which Georgia Governor refused to serve black customers in his Atlanta restaurant?

19. What was the name of Inspector Gadget's niece?

20. What is the name of the NFL team from Cincinnati?

Curious Questions 8

1. What does GBNF stand for?

2. In what year was the NHS founded?

3. What Greek physician is known as 'The Father of Medicine'?

4. When a website is NSFW, what does that stand for?

5. In what year was the Bangladesh Liberation War?

6. Who was Jimmy Carter's Vice President?

"You can't beat a bit of Bully!"

7. Who has received a record 79 Grammy nominations?

8. In 2004, a massacre took place at what Russian school?

9. How many members of Oasis were there in the classic line-up?

10. What date is VJ Day in the UK?

11. What V is the name to the skirt around a bed?

12. Which early 1960s cartoon was loosely based on *The Phil Silvers Show*?

13. In what year did Max Miller die?

14. What was the name of the Roman Road that ran from London to York?

15. What does UFO stand for?

16. As of 2016, how many children does Mel Gibson have?

17. The Film *Dreams from my real father* puts forward the theory that who was Barack Obama's Dad?

18. In what city would you find Boboli Gardens?

19. What was Peter Sutcliffe nicknamed?

20. How is Norville Rogers better known?

Curious Questions 9

1. What is the name of the most famous Geyser in Yellowstone National Park?

2. It is said that Tatum O'Neal was whose first girlfriend?

3. Who coached Joe McElderry on *The X Factor*?

4. What 1970s film starred Edward Woodward, Britt Ekland, Diane Cilento, Ingrid Pitt, and Christopher Lee?

5. What is the largest ethnic group of South Africa?

6. Who is the lead singer of Duran Duran?

7. Who shot Gandhi?

8. What was the original name of Tasmania?

9. Who is Geri Halliwell's husband?

10. St Peter Port is the capital of what island?

11. Who won BBC Sports Personality of the 20th Century?

12. Who officiated at Patrick Stewart's 2013 wedding?

13. Which city do you associate with Ken Dodd?

14. Where did the *Pied Piper* story take place?

15. What was Muhammad Ali's name at birth?

16. Who founded Earth, Wind and Fire?

17. The name 'Moonie' is used to refer to members of what Church?

18. What city is the state capital of Georgia?

19. Who is Bute, Montana's most famous son?

20. As of 2016, when was the last year that Bolton Wanderers won a major trophy?

"Remember, you can't beat a bit of Bully!"

Curious Questions 10

1. Who did Chris Evans marry in 2001?

2. What could Jack Spratt not eat?

3. Where did Jesus and the Disciples sleep on the night before the crucifixion?

4. *The Simpsons* was originally just a segment on which other show?

5. Pliny the Elder was killed during which event?

6. What phenomenon is sometimes referred to as an NDE?

7. What city is the capital of the state of Florida?

8. What Cumbrian village is known as the home of Sticky Toffee pudding?

9. Who was Larry Fortensky married to?

10. Who did Elvira, Mistress of the Darkness lose her virginity to?

11. What is the biggest country on Earth?

12. What shape is Earth?

13. Which Soldier died after overindulging at a feast in 323BC?

14. What city is the headquarters of Procter & Gamble?

15. What major river runs from South Northamptonshire to The Wash?

16. Who played Max in *Mad Max: Fury Road*?

17. What is the name of Liverpool's Airport?

18. Who were the first cartoon characters to have a No. 1 hit in the charts?

19. Which scouse medium conducted a live séance on Sky to try and contact Michael Jackson?

20. Which boxer appears on the cover of the Sgt. Pepper album?

"Bully's bellowed you out there!"

Curious Questions 11

1. What is gouda?

2. Who was 'the face that launched a thousand ships'?

3. In Greek myth, what nine sisters are the daughters of Mnemosyne?

4. A Geyser is a spring characterized by intermittent discharge of water ejected turbulently and accompanied by steam. Where is the original "Geyser" from which all others take their name?

5. What lozenge is made in Fleetwood, Lancashire?

6. Which Spice Girl has a daughter called Scarlet?

7. Who are 'the World's Leading Art Business'?

8. What is the most populous city in Alaska?

9. Did Phil Neville play more games for Manchester United or Everton?

10. Where was Florence Nightingale born?

11. What is a spud?

12. How often does a census take place?

13. What is a group of parrots called?

14. Who is Julia Roberts' acting brother?

15. When Elvis saw his new haircut complete with Sideburns, he proclaimed he looked like which other singer?

16. Which politician is most often credited for sparking the resurgence of the American conservative political movement in the 1960s?

17. In what year did *Cheers* finish?

18. Who has children called Harvey, Junior, Princess, Bunny and Jet?

19. Whose enemy was Dr. Claw?

20. What was the Centennial year of the Nobel Committee?

"101 or more with 6 darts for tonight's mystery star prize"

Curious Questions 12

1. Who were the two brothers in Oasis?

2. Which Irish businessman was once a major shareholder in Manchester United but now owns Celtic Football Club?

3. What crashes from the ceiling to provide one of the highlights of Lloyd Webber's *The Phantom of the Opera*?

4. How many people were originally in Westlife?

5. Which Minister resigned shortly after the 2016 March Budget?

"Let's check that with Bully"

6. What Australian actress was married to Sean Connery?

7. What traditional Russian instrument looks like a triangular guitar?

8. What nickname is given to the area of Manhattan also known as Midtown West?

9. What North Eastern town took its name because it was the main residence of the Bishops of Durham?

10. What country offered Albert Einstein its presidency in 1952?

11. Who was Gary Neville's netball playing sister?

12. On your TV, what does BBC stand for?

13. What was King's Lynn known as until 1537?

14. What Avian saying means something whose sensitivity to adverse conditions makes it a useful early indicator of such conditions?

15. Who was nicknamed 'The Lady With The Lamp'?

16. What age was Gandhi when he was killed?

17. What UK Christian Music Festival is usually held on the August Bank Holiday Weekend?

18. In what year did Chairman Mao die?

19. What did Craig David do on Tuesday in the song *Seven Days*?

20. In Architecture, what name is given to a central stone or other piece at the apex of an arch or vault?

Curious Questions 13

1. Who directed *The Passion*?

2. What is the difference between an American roulette wheel and a European roulette wheel?

3. Who directed *Mulholland Drive*?

4. Who invented the Roulette Wheel?

5. What was Hank Marvin's real name?

6. Who played Alf Garnett?

7. What town is the county town of Norfolk?

8. Who sang *The Boys of Summer*?

9. Who else, other than Gregg Wallace, has presented *Masterchef* since 2005?

10. What international award did President Theodore Roosevelt win in 1906?

11. Who created *Tintin*?

12. What was Gareth Hunt's character name in *The New Avengers*?

13. Who directed Eddie Murphy in *Vampire in Brooklyn*?

14. What is usually the highest attended college football bowl game?

15. The Egyptian plover is a bird best known for its symbiotic relationship with what host animal?

16. Who led The Shadows?

17. In 1993, who did *TV Guide* name as the best dramatic television actor of the 1980s?

18. Mycology is the study of what?

19. Who was the first Catholic to lead the Conservative Party?

20. What is the Duke of Buccleuch's seat in Northamptonshire?

"The subjects that are lit are the ones you can hit!"

Curious Questions 14

1. What is the highest number on a Roulette wheel?

2. In what town would you find Yale University?

3. Which river is the principal tributary of the Potomac?

4. What became the first National Park in the US?

5. Who lives in a pineapple under the sea?

"Go for your lights"

6. What song is traditionally sang by Scouts and Brownies around the campfire?

7. What were the reputed last words of the Captain of the Titanic?

8. Who played Bela Lugosi in *Ed Wood*?

9. In what year did Myleene Klass appear in *I'm a Celebrity*?

10. What were the Christian names of Abbott and Costello?

11. What two words are said to be the last uttered by Gandhi?

12. Which Max was a major influence on Ken Dodd?

13. What nickname is often given to Roger Bacon?

14. What human organs are affected by glaucoma?

15. What was Walter Kronkite famous for?

16. What is the common name for the disease rubella?

17. How many people reached the top of Mount Everest in 2005?

18. What W is a person who exposes any kind of information or activity that is deemed illegal, unethical, or not correct within an organization?

19. In what year were Nobel Prizes first awarded?

20. Who got into trouble for a 'Bag Lady' joke at the 2016 BAFTAs?

Curious Questions 15

1. What is Tchaikovsky's ballet *Le Lac des Cygnes* commonly called?

2. Which English War Poet died on the way to Gallipoli in 1915?

3. John McEnroe's middle name is Patrick. What is his brother's full name?

4. The name for which form of entertainment is derived from the Italian burla, which means 'ridicule or mockery'?

5. What is the nation's favourite dog contest?

6. At what WW1 battle was poison gas first used?

7. Which US president was nicknamed 'Big Bill'?

"You've had a good night out - but you go home with nowt!"

8. According to the *Guinness Book of Records*, where would we find the largest ancient castle in the world?

9. How many players in a Shinty team?

10. Who had hits with *Fox on the Run* and *Ballroom Blitz*?

11. In which county will you find the town of Ross-on-Wye?

12. Which character is depicted as an anthropomorphic white Japanese bobtail cat?

13. Linda Tripp was a key player in what scandal?

14. What was the language of Jesus?

15. Which comedy character of the 90s has been described as 'a child in a grown man's body'?

16. In America, the Republican Party is sometimes referred to as the 'GOP', what does GOP stand for?

17. At school, Iain Duncan Smith played in the same rugby side as which other famous person?

18. What was the name of the American version of *The Upper Hand*?

19. What is the American version of *Strictly Come Dancing*?

20. The Hall of Mirrors is the largest room in what famous structure?

Curious Questions 16

1. What bank did Abbey National become?

2. What major war memorial is located on Whitehall, London?

3. What animal did Will Ferrell enact as for his audition on *Saturday Night Live*?

4. What is Shakin' Stevens' real name?

5. What do Americans call a pram/ buggy?

6. Matthew Barzun is the current holder of which post?

7. What does AM stand for, as in 'the time was 9am'?

"Throwers and Knowers"

8. What town lies on the southern bank of the Tyne, opposite Newcastle?

9. Which partly animated 2009 film became the highest grossing film of all time?

10. What type of performances would you associate with Jonathan Goodwin?

11. Which format lost the Videotape Format War?

12. In the Diary page of *The Times*, what time is showing on the clock?

13. What Welsh City is regarded as Britain's smallest city in terms of both size and population?

14. What was the name of Gary and Philip Neville's Dad?

15. Complete the Joke: 'A Roman walks into a bar, holds up two fingers and says…'

16. Naomi Watts' father was the road manager for which famous band?

17. Who left Atomic Kitten just as they were having their breakthrough?

18. What search engine is believed to be the most popular website in the World?

19. What were the surnames of Bonnie and Clyde?

20. What American city is approximately 120 miles (190 km) south of Los Angeles and immediately adjacent to the border with Mexico?

Curious Questions 17

"It's a bulllllseye! And here's your host - Jiiiim Bowen!"

1. Who was the lead singer of Wet Wet Wet?

2. True or false, Nigel Planer appeared in Downton Abbey?

3. Which twins successfully sued Mark Zuckerberg for $65m?

4. Who created *Grange Hill*?

5. The name of what country translates as (Republic of) The Saviour?

6. What football team does Mel C support?

7. Which comedian gave us the character 'Basildon Bond'?

8. What was the name of Christopher Walken's character in *A View To A Kill*?

9. Who was the 'Godfather of Soul'?

10. Peter Ustinov was married to which actress' half sister?

11. Who was the Supreme Commander of the Allied Forces in Europe in WW2?

12. How is Asa Yoelson better known?

13. Which sportsman's autobiography is titled *You Cannot Be Serious*?

14. What is *Mad Max*'s surname?

15. Who wrote *The Invisible Man*?

16. Who is Ozzy Osbourne's wife?

17. What revolution started in China in 1966?

18. What book facilitated the ban of the pesticide DDT in 1972 in the U.S.?

19. What nationality has won more Nobel Prizes than any other?

20. Who won a record eight gold medals at the 2008 Summer Olympics in Beijing?

Curious Questions 18

1. In a 2013 survey, what percentage of Americans identified themselves as Irish Americans?

2. What is the parent company of Cadbury's?

3. Who wrote *Pennies From Heaven* and *The Singing Detective*?

4. The Pritzker Prize is an award given in what field?

5. According to the RIAA, who is the 3rd top selling solo music artist in the USA?

6. Which cartoon featuring the Spanish language first appeared in 2000?

7. Who played *Oscar Wilde* in the 1997 film?

8. Which producer is Michael Jackson most associated with?

9. Who was the crack smoking mayor of Toronto?

10. Who was the lead singer of The Sweet?

11. Which gravel-voiced TV Dragon owned Pall-ex?

12. What award is given to the best show at the Edinburgh Festival Fringe each year?

13. In what year was BBC2 launched?

14. Geoffrey Boycott is sometimes referred to as 'GLY'. What does GLY stand for?

15. In what year were Pringles first sold?

16. Who wrote *Silent Spring*?

17. Who played Christine in the original Broadway cast of *The Phantom of The Opera*?

18. The Eisner Award is an award given in what field?

19. What kind of animal is a Beltie?

20. Which famous Businessman is buried in Highcliffe, Dorset?

> "Stay out of the black and into the red, nothing in this game for two in a bed."

England and Wales 1

1. Highclere Castle was the setting for *Downton Abbey*. In which county can Highclere Castle be found?

2. What is the national drink of Wales?

3. Which English National Park contains all the land in England over 3000ft?

4. In which English county would we find the historic town of Sandwich?

5. Where in Surrey will you find The Lakeside Country Club?

6. Where is the longest cathedral in the world?

7. Where in Wales did a disaster kill 116 children in 1966?

8. In what town would the headquarters of Tesco be found?

9. What name is given to the naturally marshy region around The Wash?

10. What is the second biggest city in Wales?

11. What colour strip does the Welsh Rugby team wear?

12. In which county is the town of Sevenoaks?

13. Where does a smoggie come from?

14. The steel for Blackpool Tower was made in which northeast town?

15. What is the longest river entirely in Wales?

16. Which school has had the highest Oxford and Cambridge acceptance rates of any secondary school or college in the world?

17. In which Welsh town do the 'Ironsides' rugby team play?

18. Which English park has the longest lime tree avenue in Europe?

19. What landmark is the central focus for the celebrations in Oxford on May Morning?

20. What is England's largest inland county?

"Innnnnn three..."

England and Wales 2

1. A corner at Silverstone Racecourse is named after which prestigious school?

2. What does a Welsh person want if they ask for a 'cwtch'?

3. Which North East vernacular developed as a separate dialect from Northumbrian and Geordie partly due to the specialised terms used by mineworkers in the local coal pits?

4. What is the nearest town to Burghley House?

5. How do we normally refer to the Welsh Island of Ynys Mons?

6. In what city did the Peterloo Massacre take place?

7. What area roughly comprises the counties of Norfolk, Suffolk and Cambridgeshire?

8. Which large Midlands city was granted that status as part of Queen Victoria's Diamond Jubilee celebrations?

9. What is the oldest known inhabited part of Wales?

10. What Lincolnshire town is known as the 'Industrial Garden Town'?

11. David Platt the footballer and Brian Cox the scientist are both from what Lancashire town?

12. The "Welsh Streets" is an area of what city?

13. How long is the coastline of South Yorkshire?

14. The Hillsborough Disaster was a tragedy in 1989. In which city did it occur?

15. What is the highest point on the Southern Coast of England?

16. What river runs through Sheffield?

17. What viaduct carries the Settle-Carlisle Railway across Batty Moss?

18. In which Yorkshire town was Jeremy Clarkson born?

19. The English town of Preston has the same etymological route as the name of which Welsh resort?

20. What is the largest settlement in Leicestershire outside the city of Leicester?

"You win nothing but your BFH... Bus Fare Home"

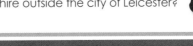

England and Wales 3

1. In which Yorkshire village was Roy Castle born?

2. The name of which Cornish village means Pyra's cove?

3. Which English seaside resort was the first to open a nudist beach in 1979?

4. In which county is the town of Eastbourne?

5. What cathedral featured in *The Omen*?

6. In which county was Captain Cook born?

7. Which cathedral has the longest Nave in Europe?

8. What island off the north east coast of England is also known as 'Holy Island'?

9. What is the second largest town in the county of Buckinghamshire after Milton Keynes?

10. What is the largest town in the TW postcode area?

11. What green foodstuff has been referred to as Yorkshire Caviar?

12. Who was the oldest player in England's winning 1966 World Cup team?

13. In which Yorkshire town does Dracula reach the shores of England?

14. On what river does the town of Wetherby stand?

15. What is the largest island in Wales?

16. In which Yorkshire battle did American hero John Paul Jones have one of his finest moments?

17. What runs from Starr Gate at the south end of the town to Bispham in the north?

18. What is the most easterly point in Yorkshire?

19. Where will you find the longest breakwater in the UK?

20. The largest cluster of Ogham script inscriptions outside of Ireland are found in which Welsh county?

England and Wales 4

1. Where in Britain will you find the Rotherhithe Tunnel?

2. In what English town would you find The Stump?

3. What is the largest town in Cheshire?

4. Which Welsh TV Presenter was engaged to Katherine Jenkins?

5. In what area of London is Lord's Cricket Ground?

6. Which Cornish village is regarded as the most southerly port on the island of Great Britain?

7. Briggate is the principle shopping street in which north English city?

8. In which county is Windsor Castle?

9. What city is sometimes known as Brum?

10. What is unusual about Chesterfield Parish Church?

"All for the throw of a dart"

11. The New Forest is mostly in which county?

12. Which North Yorks RAF base hosts the Ballistic Missile Early Warning System?

13. Where is Charterhouse School located?

14. What county town is situated 12 miles north of Cardiff?

15. From what Yorkshire town do the 'Chuckle Brothers' hail?

16. In which county is 'Beckingham Palace'?

17. Stockton is an area of which city?

18. Which valley of North Yorkshire is known for its cheese?

19. What is the largest island in England?

20. In which area of Cardiff does the Welsh Assembly sit?

Family Ties

1. Who is married to Charlie Brooker?

2. Who was Johnny Dankworth's wife?

3. Who is Boris Johnson's MP brother?

4. Who is Kim Kardashian's godfather?

5. Who is DJ Janice Long's famous brother?

"Up to the oche - and listen to Tony!"

6. Who is married to singer Amanda Palmer?

7. Who was married to Renate Blauel between 1984 and 1988?

8. Who is Isla Fisher married to?

9. What is the name of Dick Van Dyke's son, his co-star in *Diagnosis Murder*?

10. Who is Loretta Lynn's famous sister?

11. Who is former Dr Who Peter Davison's son-in-law?

12. Who is Lionel Richie's Socialite adopted daughter?

13. Who was Hank Azaria married to from 1999 to 2000?

14. Who was Katy Perry married to from 2010 to 2012?

15. Who is Jane Goldman married to?

16. What is the name of Madonna's son with Guy Ritchie?

17. What surname is shared by acting brothers Alec, Daniel, Billy and Stephen?

18. How many children did Charlie Chaplin have?

19. Who is Beyonce's husband?

20. Who is Victoria Coren Mitchell's brother?

Famous Barrys

1. How is Barack Obama allegedly named on his School Yearbook?

2. Which famous Barry would you associate with football and tennis commentary?

3. Which famous Barry was one of the top British Motorcycle racers of the 1970s?

4. Who played *Eastenders'* legend Barry Evans?

5. Which famous Barry played Brad in *The Rocky Horror Picture Show*?

6. Which famous Barry was a writer for Morecambe & Wise?

7. Which famous Barry was born Barry Pincus?

8. Which famous Barry was The Clones Cyclone?

9. Which Barry character is the face of Cillit Bang?

"You can't beat a bit of Bully!"

10. Which famous Barry ran for US President in 1964?

11. Which famous Barry was one of Britain's top bookies until retirement in 2011?

12. Which famous Barry played for both Sunderland and Newcastle over 100 times?

13. Which famous Barry was born in Rotherham in 1944?

14. Which famous Barry played *Van Der Valk*?

15. Which Barry has the second highest tidal range of anywhere in the world?

16. Which Barry was the leader of The Bee Gees?

17. Which famous Barry's international career ended when he made a rude sign on TV?

18. Which famous Barry gave us Dame Edna Everage?

19. Which Barry played 25 times for Wales and is regarded as one of their greatest ever players?

20. Which famous Barry was nicknamed 'the Walrus of Love'?

Films 1

1. Who directed *Midnight in the Garden of Good and Evil*?

2. Who wrote the screenplay for *Chariots of Fire*?

3. What was the sub-title of *Star Trek II* (1982)?

4. Which 1991 film featured Hannibal the Cannibal?

5. In 1986, who directed *The Color of Money*?

6. What film ends with 'Frankly my dear, I don't give a damn'?

7. Who played 'Danny' in *High Heels and Low Lifes*?

8. Which movie gave us the term 'a bunny boiler'?

9. Who directed *The Untouchables*?

10. Who directed *The Grand Budapest Hotel*?

"101 or more with 6 darts for tonight's mystery star prize"

11. 'What did the Romans ever do for us' is a famous scene in what film?

12. In how many *James Bond* films did Sean Connery star?

13. Which 2014 film starred Ralph Fiennes as a hotel concierge?

14. What does the BFI rank as the best ever British film?

15. Which film featured The Battle of Rorke's Drift?

16. How many *Harry Potter* films were there?

17. How many Oscars did *The Bridge on the River Kwai* win?

18. Who starred in *Cape Fear*?

19. In which fictional resort was *Jaws* set?

20. Which film had its premiere in Stirling in 1995?

Films 2

1. To date, who is the youngest person to play James Bond?

2. Which conman was the subject of the film *Catch Me If You Can*?

3. Who starred in the 1939 film *Gunga Din*?

4. What series of films follows a secret organisation who monitor alien activity on Earth?

"Let's check that with Bully"

5. Which film starred Nicole Kidman and featured Eric Sykes?

6. Who was the female star of *Zero Dark Thirty*?

7. In what decade does the movie *Girl, Interrupted* take place?

8. Which 1978 film starred Terence Stamp and Gene Hackman amongst others?

9. Who was the star of *Risky Business*?

10. What was the subtitle of the sequel to *Arthur*?

11. Did *Saving Private Ryan* win the Best Film Oscar?

12. Which 2000s film follows two men who take a week-long road trip to Santa Barbara County Wine Country?

13. What was Dick Van Dyke's character name in *Mary Poppins*?

14. Who directed *Cocoon* and *A Beautiful Mind*?

15. Vincent Price starred in seven adaptations of whose work in the 1960s?

16. Who played *Mad Max* in three 1980s films?

17. Which character did Tobin Bell play in the *Saw* films?

18. Which actor has appeared in more of the BFI's Top 100 British films than any other?

19. In what year was both *The Breakfast Club* and *Weird Science* released?

20. Who made his directorial debut with the drama *Badlands*?

Films 3

1. Which body-building actor from Glasgow, Montana was mentioned in *The Rocky Horror Picture Show*?

2. Whose first major film role came in the 1981 romantic drama *The French Lieutenant's Woman*?

3. What are the names of the gangs in *West Side Story*?

4. What 1986 comedy was directed by Francis Ford Coppola?

5. Which film holds the record for the most number of extras used?

"It's a bulllllseye! And here's your host - Jiiiim Bowen!"

6. Who played *Shaft* in the 2000 sequel/ remake?

7. What fruit symbolises Death in *The Godfather Trilogy*?

8. Who played evil Cal Hockley in the 1997 movie *Titanic*?

9. Which film gave us the odd pairing of Estelle Getty and Sylvester Stallone?

10. What was the first film to win all 5 major Academy Awards?

11. Who was the young star of *Candleshoe*?

12. What nationality was film director Stanley Kubrick?

13. Who provided the voice of the baby girl in *Look Who's Talking Too*?

14. What was the last *Harry Potter* film in the series?

15. What was Rocky's nickname?

16. Who won the very first Best Director Oscar?

17. Which actor is famous for hanging from the hands of a clock in *Safety Last*?

18. In which 2012 film do two people with problems learn more about relationships as they train together for a dance competition?

19. Who directed *Big Trouble in Little China*?

20. What film brought back together the stars and director of *Pretty Woman*?

Films 4

1. Rachel Marron is the singer who needs protecting in which 90s movie?

2. Who directed *Driving Miss Daisy*?

3. Who played *Fletch* in 1980s films?

4. Which actress starred in five of the *Fast and Furious* films?

5. What city does *The Wizard of Oz* live in?

6. Who played JMW Turner in the film *Mr Turner*?

7. Which Martial Artist starred in *The Delta Force*?

8. In which film is Jake Gyllenhaal confronted by a monstrous rabbit?

9. What 1995 action comedy was one of the biggest flops of all time?

10. Who played 'Begbie' in *Trainspotting*?

11. What was the first Pixar prequel?

12. Who played Jesus in *The Last Temptation of Christ*?

13. Ben Affleck and George Clooney were producers on which 2010 Oscar winning film?

14. Whose legs doubled for Anne Bancroft's in *The Graduate*?

15. Who directed *The Aviator*?

16. What film was the first adaptation of the Hannibal Lecter novels?

17. In which film did Madonna play *Breathless*?

18. Marvin Nash is a character in which Quentin Tarantino film?

19. Which character is *The Terminator* sent to kill in the film of the same name?

20. Who directed *The Full Monty*?

> "Stay out of the black and into the red, nothing in this game for two in a bed."

Films 5

1. In what year was the film *Carlito's Way* released?

2. What veteran star of stage and screen played the mastermind behind *The Italian Job*?

3. Which film won the BAFTA for best film in 2015?

4. Which 70s horror film had characters called Jupiter, Pluto, Mars and Mercury?

5. What film series introduced us to Chucky the murderous doll?

6. Who directed *The Shining*?

7. What horror film franchise starred Tobin Bell?

8. Who was the first black man to win a Best Director Oscar?

9. From 1959 to 1964, who was Doris Day's co-star in three romantic comedies?

10. What is the highest grossing Christmas movie of all time at the North American box office?

11. Who directed *Sleepy Hollow*?

12. Who was the female star of the 1985 film *Red Sonja*?

13. Which film followed Cheryl Strayed's hike on the Pacific Crest Trail?

14. Which film made us an offer we couldn't refuse?

15. How was Jordan Belfort referred to in a 2013 film?

16. Who played Wednesday Addams in *The Addams Family* (1991)?

17. Which film looked at the success of Baseball Coach Billy Beane?

18. The film *Badlands* uses which composer's Glockenspiel music?

19. Who won the Best Director Oscar for *The Life of Pi*?

20. What is the name of the hotel in *The Shining*?

"Look at what you could have won."

Food and Drink 1

"And Bully's Special Priiiiize..."
Food!

1. What is the study of food called?

2. What is the Chinese gooseberry?

3. Which food would you associate with the company Lindt?

4. What frothy tea drink often has chewy balls added?

5. The name of which food product derives from the French term for a large, covered earthenware or metal cooking pot?

6. What dish is the official cuisine of the state of Louisiana?

7. What popular central European dish could be described as a soup or stew seasoned with paprika?

8. Which breakfast dish consists of smoked fish, boiled rice, eggs, curry powder & butter?

9. What fruit do you get by crossing a raspberry with a blackberry?

10. In what year was the Freddo Frog chocolate bar invented?

11. What is the name of beetroot soup?

12. What is a Porterhouse?

13. What chocolate bar did Cadbury's bring out to take on the Aero?

14. What do we call the food item usually made up of one or more fillings placed between two pieces of bread?

15. What sauce did Levi Roots promote?

16. What name is given to someone who abstains from the use of all animal products?

17. Kopi Luwak is a very expensive type of what drink?

18. What non-alcoholic drink is traditionally made with ginger ale, a splash of grenadine and garnished with a maraschino cherry?

19. Filbert is an alternative name for which common nut?

20. What seeds are on the bun of a Big Mac?
Sesame seeds.

Food and Drink 2

"Now the cash you won for charity earlier... that's safe."

1. What is the national dish of Vietnam?

2. What is couscous made from?

3. What is quark?

4. What spice is named for the capital of French Guiana?

5. Which chocolate bar consists of nougat and rice crispies covered in chocolate?

6. What Welsh dish is made by boiling seaweed for several hours?

7. The name of what soup translates as pepper water?

8. What food would you associate with Papa John?

9. A 2014 study found what was the most popular flavour of crisps?

10. What food could be Lorne, Cumberland or Blood?

11. What type of food could be called a ruby?

12. What dish normally consists of prawns, chicken and rice?

13. What type of flour is used to make pasta?

14. What fruit did Algerian priest Pierre Clement create in 1902?

15. From which city does Coleman's mustard hail?

16. What is the main ingredient of guacomole?
    Avacado

17. Which Cypriot cheese is often made from goats' milk?

18. What drink would you associate with John Pemberton?

19. What type of pastry is used to make profiteroles?

20. What is a bannock?

Football

1. What football team play their home games on The Wirral?

2. In what city do Bohemian FC play?

3. Roger Milla helped which side become the first African team to get to the World Cup Quarter Finals?

4. Who did Gary Lineker sign for in 1992?

5. Who managed the Scottish national football team from 1993 to 2001?

6. Which team plays at Dean Court?

7. Who played 119 games for Northern Ireland as a goalkeeper?

8. Which ground was reportedly the first floodlit stadium?

9. Who did Arsenal sign from Celtic in 1983?

10. Of which team was Elton John the chairman?

11. At which ground do Liverpool play?

"Super, smashing, great."

12. What was the last British club that George Best scored a goal for?

13. Which goalkeeper holds the unusual record of winning a trophy in his only game as a manager?

14. What report recommended that all major stadiums go to all-seater?

15. Who is the youngest player to take part in a World Cup?

16. Who was Scotland's first choice keeper at the 1990 World Cup?

17. After Barcelona and Real Madrid, which team have won the Spanish league the most times?

18. Who did England defeat in the 1996 Football World Cup Final?

19. Where do Birmingham City play?

20. What was footballer Liam Brady's real first name?

General Knowledge 1

1. Who asked the quiz questions on television's *The Weakest Link*?

2. Dennis the Menace featured in which British children's comic?

3. Desperate Dan featured in which British comic?

4. What is a funambulist?

5. What C would Americans call a block of flats?

6. In which month of 1945 did Hitler marry Eva Braun?

"101 or more with 6 darts for tonight's mystery star prize"

7. What French term is used to describe a small living unit usually located in a large city some distance away from an individual's primary residence?

8. Which television and radio quiz show for schools ran from 1948 to 1986?

9. The Bella Twins are famous professionals in which field?

10. What does MDF stand for (as in the engineered wood product)?

11. Which U.S. President wrote a foreign policy doctrine regarding European countries in 1823?

12. Who is Alexander Armstrong's seated assistant on the gameshow *Pointless*?

13. What nationality is Mark Carney, The Governor of the Bank of England?

14. Which company was founded in Birmingham in 1892 by Frederick Rushbrooke?

15. Who asks the quiz questions on *University Challlenge*?

16. In English, what do the initials of the car manufacturer BMW stand for?

17. Andy Millman is the main character in which British sitcom?

18. What is Harry Ramsden famous for?

19. Daniel Hooper was Britain's most famous Environmental Activist, how was he better known?

20. What colour is the Welsh word coch?

General Knowledge 2

1. What Channel 4 programme was described by the *Daily Mail* as 'the most intelligent, thought-provoking and interesting programme ever to have been on television'?

2. Name the largest town in the Highlands of Scotland?

3. Which weekly magazine of humour and satire was established in 1841 and ceased publication in 2002?

4. Who was MP for Tatton before Martin Bell won the seat in 1997?

5. Which London Borough's name is famous for British comedy films in the 50s & 60s?

6. In which body of water would you be if you were at 0 deg Longitude, 0 deg Latitude?

7. Which city is at the area where the Mississippi river meets the Missouri river?

8. What did British Honduras become when it gained independence?

9. Which two countries could offer a Dead Sea beach holiday?

"All for the throw of a dart"

10. Who provided the voice of the baby in *Look Who's Talking*?

11. Who was Whoopie Goldberg hiding from in *Sister Act*?

12. How old was Tom Hanks's character in *Big*?

13. What was the name of Inspector Clouseau's boss?

14. Who were the two main stars of *Trains Planes & Automobiles*?

15. In which year did John Candy die?

16. What is the last event of a decathlon?

17. The battle of Bosworth Field in 1485 was the last battle of which war?

18. What was Marilyn Monroe's name at birth?

19. Who was the last person to join the Rolling Stones?

20. Which comedian had the biggest selling single of 1965?

General Knowledge 3

1. *Brass In Pocket* was a number one for which band in 1979?

2. Matt, Luke & Craig were the three members of which 80s boy band?

3. Which group took England's World Cup Squad to No. 1 in 1990 with *World In Motion*?

4. Which cartoon superhero does Eric the schoolboy turn into?

5. Which fictional character went to Greyfriars School?

6. Which member of the public became famous after starring in the documentary *Driving School*?

7. Which school has provided Britain with 19 Prime Ministers?

8. Named after an element, what was the name of the USA's first manned space programme?

9. Which animal name means river horse?

10. What is the natural habitat of arboreal creatures?

"Go for your lights"

11. Copper is named after which Mediterranean island?

12. Graeme Garden & Bill Oddie are two of *The Goodies* – who was the third?

13. In which modern country would the Hanging Gardens of Babylon be if they still existed?

14. Who designed the *Blue Peter* garden in BBC Television Centre?

15. William Henry Pratt is the real name of which horror actor?

16. Warden Hodges in *Dad's Army* is related in real life to which Dr Who actor?

17. Which TV cartoon series features Stan, Kyle, Kenny & Eric?

18. Dr Teeth & Electric Mayhem were the resident band on which TV show?

19. Who was the lead singer of the Australian group The Seekers?

20. Who wrote the music for the musical *Top Hat!*?

General Knowledge 4

1. Man Utd paid £29m for which Leeds player in 2002?

2. Which 30s actress was known as the blonde bombshell after her debut in Platinum Blond?

3. If you travel due east from Glasgow which country do you reach first?

4. Victoria Falls are on the border between Zimbabwe and which other country?

5. The Great Barrier Reef lies off the coast of which Australian State?

6. Which clothing discount stores were founded by John Hargreaves in 1985 in Preston?

7. How many hours did Playtex claim their famous girdle could be worn for?

8. Which brand of toys were known as real tough toys for real tough boys?

9. Which chain of shops logo is a red apple with a small bite taken out?

10. Which event did Sally Gunnell win her Olympic gold medal?

11. What was the 3rd London club that Jimmy Greaves played for after Chelsea & Spurs?

12. Who won the Stanley Cup in 2015?

13. Who did Cassius Clay defeat to become world champion in 1964?

14. Peter Fleming was the doubles partner for many years with which tennis player?

15. In the 60s, whose backing group were the Blue Flames?

16. Which boy's name was Blondie's first big hit?

17. Who was Cilla Black's first manager?

18. The film *A Man For All Seasons* is about whom?

19. Which Yorkshireman played the IRA terrorist in the film *Patriot Games*?

20. How many orbits did Yuri Gagarin complete in Vostok 1?

"You've got the time it takes for the board to revolve..."

General Knowledge 5

1. How many Apollo missions successfully landed on the moon?

2. Which planet's moons are named after Shakespearean characters?

3. The radio telescope Jodrell Bank belongs to which university?

4. What gives the cheese Red Windsor its red colour?

5. Which pasta shape is fusilli?

"Look at what you could have won."

6. Who was elected leader of the Labour Party in November 1980?

7. What was the name of the musical based on the music of Madness?

8. Which England rugby player won *Celebrity Masterchef* on BBC 1 in 2006?

9. What date is *Back to the Future* Day?

10. What date is sometimes referred to as *Star Wars* Day?

11. In which decade was HIV identified by scientists?

12. In which decade was the modern bikini introduced?

13. In which decade was Amy Winehouse born?

14. Which industrial process allowed the production of steel from molten pig iron?

15. In the tale *Jack and the Beanstalk*, what did Jack trade for the magic beans?

16. What did *Old King Cole* call for?

17. In which country were The Brothers Grimm born?

18. What does Zorro mean in Spanish?

19. Luxembourg has its roots in what other language?

20. What does Yoga mean in Sanskrit?

General Knowledge 6

1. What does *Tierra del Fuego* mean in English?

2. What is the plural of deer?

3. Which large character in *Lost* was played by Jorge Garcia?

4. Which large actor starred in *Uncle Buck* and *Planes, Trains and Automobiles*?

5. Who played more games for Manchester United, Roy Keane or Paul Scholes?

6. What is the cube root of 27?

7. What is 11 x 11?

8. How many degrees in a semi-circle?

9. What colour is Vine Street on a Monopoly board?

10. In what year was the Boxing Day Tsunami?

11. What is the nickname of Radio DJ David Jensen?

12. Which nursery rhyme tells us about the little boy who lives down the lane?

13. Where would you find the Sea of Tranquillity?

14. In which pub did Ronnie Kray murder George Cornell?

15. What radio station broadcasts on 1089 AM?

16. In which fictional county is *The Archers* set?

17. Who presented the mid-morning program on Radio 5 Live for 16 years until 2014?

18. In what year was Radio 5 launched?

19. *Sailing by* is a piece of music played before which Radio 4 institution?

20. Who is the longest serving Radio One Breakfast show host?

"You can't beat a bit of Bully!"

General Knowledge 7

1. What is the radio equivalent of *Points of View*?

2. On which AM frequency does Absolute Radio broadcast?

3. Who wrote *The Hitchikers Guide to the Galaxy*?

4. Who played Rambling Syd Rumpo in *Round the Horne*?

5. Who is the main presenter associated with *Ramblings* on Radio 4?

6. What nickname is given to a radio presenter who deliberately sets out to cause offence to a portion of the listeners?

7. What Z is a whacky radio format?

8. Who is the current presenter of *Just a Minute*?

9. Tim Smith and Janey Lee Grace are whose sidekicks on radio?

10. Who is the moneylender in *The Merchant of Venice*?

11. In which city is *A Midsummer Night's Dream* set?

12. On which Shakespeare play is *West Side Story* based?

13. What is Spanish for beer?

14. What is German for 'I love you'?

15. From what language does the word honcho derive, as in 'he was the head honcho of our gang'?

16. From which language did English borrow the word rodeo?

17. What is the German word for Empire?

18. Under what nom de plume did Stephen King write *The Running Man*?

19. What was the name of the rabid dog character King created in 1981?

20. What is the name of Tony Stark's assistant in the *Iron Man* films?

"Remember, you can't beat a bit of Bully!"

General Knowledge 8

1. Who did the IRA kill on the 27th November 1975?

2. Which English football club did Osama Bin Laden supposedly support?

3. Where were 30 Britons killed in a terrorist attack in June 2015?

4. Who said, 'The true measure of a man is how he treats someone who can do him absolutely no good'?

5. Who said, 'All Men are equal before Fish'?

6. The word smog is a portmanteau of which two other words?

7. What word was promoted by Thomas Edison as a proper telephone welcome?

8. In *West Side Story,* who was Maria in love with?

9. Which North East constituency is usually the first to declare results at a General Election?

10. What flavour is the liqueur Amaretto?

11. Who had a big hit with *Message in a Bottle*?

12. What is the new name of the tower that houses Big Ben?

13. 17 of the 20 highest mountains in the USA are in which state?

14. What nationality is tennis player Caroline Wosniacki?

15. Who designed and built the seaplane known as the Spruce Goose?

16. Which company which ran care homes in the UK closed in 2011 after a BBC *Panorama* show?

17. Which drink was advertised as looks good, tastes good and by golly does you good?

18. In what year was the SDP formed?

19. What was the name of the girl band imprisoned in Russia for anti government songs?

20. Who was Adolf Hitler's mentor in the early days of the Nazi Party?

"Bully's bellowed you out there!"

General Knowledge 9

1. What is the main ingredient of the Indian dish dahl?

2. Which TV characters were married to 'She who must be obeyed'?

3. Which sport features nose diving and tube riding?

4. What was the BBC's teletext information service?

5. What title did George VI hold before he became King?

6. What was ITV's version of *Ceefax*?

7. In football, who are The Tigers?

8. Which writing instrument made its first appearance in 1960?

9. In which city was Martin Luther King assassinated?

10. Which chemical element is added to steel makes it stainless steel?

11. What commemorative day is celebrated on 10th January in the Falkland Islands?

12. Uggie the dog was one of the stars of which Oscar winning film of 2012?

13. Which gay comedian won *Celebrity Big Brother* in September 2012?

14. Meryl Streep won Best Actress Oscar for playing which politician?

15. What are the names of Margaret Thatcher's children?

16. What was Psy's big hit?

17. Which trees have been severely affected by die back in recent years?

18. Who played the part of Brunel at the London 2012 Olympic opening ceremony?

19. What is the first name of President Hollande of France?

20. Who did Barack Obama defeat in the 2012 US Presidential Election?

"101 or more with 6 darts for tonight's mystery star prize"

General Knowledge 10

1. What is the name of the judge who presided over the newspaper phone-tapping enquiry?

2. Which planet did the Curiosity rover land on?

3. What was the name of the specially built barge that transported the Queen on the Thames for her Jubilee?

4. Which jazz musician was famous for the tune *Take Five*?

5. Which British singer won six Grammy's in 2012?

6. Which monarch was the first to attend Royal Ascot?

"Let's check that with Bully"

7. What was the tallest structure in the world before the Eiffel Tower was built?

8. 30 St Mary Axe in London is more commonly known by which nickname?

9. What is the largest building in the world made entirely of white marble?

10. What is the first planet mentioned in the song *Fly Me To The Moon*?

11. What does *Eleanor Rigby* keep in a jar by the door?

12. What was the name of Smokey Robinson's backing band?

13. What did Margaret Thatcher take away in 1971 when she was Education Minister?

14. Which former leader of the Liberal party stood trial for attempted murder in 1979?

15. Which savings scheme did the government introduce in 1956?

16. What is the name of the computer which picks Premium Bond winners?

17. In which decade was the first version of Microsoft Windows launched?

18. What is the main ingredient of falafel?

19. Which country produces 70% of the world's olive oil?

20. What is the name of the Spanish soup usually served chilled?

General Knowledge 11

1. Chicken Marengo is named after a battle fought by which European leader's army?

2. Who was the only Swedish player to win the Wimbledon Men's Singles title in the 90s?

3. Which American Football team play in Baltimore?

4. What was the name of the 1985 Harrison Ford film set in the Amish community?

5. What breed of dog is Snoopy?

6. What sort of animals were 'The Tamworth Two', who achieved fame in 1998?

7. What is the real surname of the Chuckle Brothers?

8. Which duo had their biggest hit in 1982 with save *Your Love*?

9. What was the name of The Kray's gang?

10. What is the name of the main railway station in Manchester?

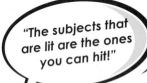

"The subjects that are lit are the ones you can hit!"

11. For what is Busby Berkeley most famous?

12. Which city in China has the largest population?

13. Which wedding anniversary is your china wedding?

14. Which gas is sometimes called marsh gas?

15. Thomas Selfridge was the first plane crash fatality, who was the pilot?

16. Who had a British number one with *Make It Easy On Yourself* in 1965?

17. Elizabeth I was the last monarch of which Royal house?

18. Which country celebrates Thanksgiving on the second Monday of October?

19. Apart from London, which three cities in the UK have hosted the Commonwealth Games?

20. Which country held Syria as a colony at the time Muammar Gaddafi was born?

General Knowledge 12

1. What is the name of the town in the TV series *Heartbeat*?

2. What type of creature is the cartoon character Foghorn Leghorn?

3. What is the name of the now decommissioned nuclear power station in Caithness?

4. Dounreay Nuclear Power station was an FBR. What does FBR stand for?

5. Which singer played Leather Tuscadero in the TV series *Happy Days*?

6. Who was famously arrested for shoplifting in 2001?

7. Apart from Harvard & Yale, can you name any other US University who are part of the Ivy League?

8. Which company was the first to sponsor a one-day cricket tournament in the UK?

9. Which black singer was the first to host their own TV series in the USA in the 50s?

10. What ship ran aground in Italy on 13th January 2012?

11. Who was host of the ITV series *Odd One In*?

12. Who is the host of the BBC show *Would I Lie To You*?

13. Which female tennis player lost seven Wimbledon Singles finals in the 70s & 80s?

14. Which Indian tribe features in *Dances With Wolves*?

15. What mental health issue is abbreviated as SAD?

16. What is the name of the murderous doll in the film *Childs' Play*?

17. In which city are the headquarters of UNICEF?

18. What is Xenophobia the fear of?

19. Which acid is found in an ant bite?

20. Which documentary maker gave us *Sicko* and *Bowling for Columbine*?

"Throwers and Knowers"

General Knowledge 13

1. What is the only US State beginning with the letter D?

2. How was Belize formerly known?

3. What David Beckham nickname is also a former TV game show?

4. What is the nickname of the Argentinian Rugby Union team?

5. Which film was about a search for the toy Turboman on Christmas Eve?

6. Who was Bing Crosby's male co-star in *White Christmas*?

7. What was the first name of the boy in *The Snowman*?

8. Which cake was created to celebrate the marriage of Queen Victoria's granddaughter Princess Victoria?

9. What traditionally sticks out of the top of a Stargazy pie?

10. Which nuts are used in a Waldorf salad?

11. Which herb is the basis for a pesto?

12. What is mascarpone?

13. Which comedian featured on a version of Smokie's "Living Next Door To Alice"?

14. Who directed *Full Metal Jacket*?

15. During the Wars of the Roses, what colour was the rose of Lancaster?

16. Which motorised new weapon was first used at the Battle of the Somme in WW1?

17. Who was the husband in *Butterflies*?

18. What was the spin-off to *Porridge* called?

19. Which comedian co-wrote the musical *We Will Rock You*?

20. Who played Amy Pond in *Doctor Who*?

"You've had a good night out - but you go home with nowt!"

General Knowledge 14

1. Which actress who starred in the film *Blue Lagoon* was Andre Agassi's first wife?

2. Which singer had a big Xmas hit with 'I Believe In Father Christmas' in 1975?

3. Which comedy actor played Clouseau in the remake of *The Pink Panther* in 2006?

4. Who starred opposite Meg Ryan in *When Harry Met Sally*?

5. In which film did Harrison Ford play President James Marshall?

"Throwers and Knowers"

6. In which athletics event is a planting box used?

7. When Glenn Hoddle was appointed England manager, who replaced him as manager of Chelsea in 1996?

8. Which World Champion British motorcycle rider was known as Mike the Bike?

9. Which *Avengers* character was played by Honor Blackman?

10. Which character was played by Arnold Schwarzenegger in *Batman & Robin*?

11. Which *Last of the Summer Wine* character was played by Brian Wilde?

12. The French city of Grasse is famous for what product which women love?

13. Which city was capital of Japan before Tokyo?

14. What was the name of the fictional Tibetan retreat in James Hilton's Lost Horizon?

15. Mary Norton wrote a series of books about which little people?

16. What was the name of the schoolboy created by Richmal Crompton?

17. The USA's highest mountain, Mt McKinley is in which state?

18. Which Womble was named after a town in Siberia?

19. On which river does the Kariba Dam in Africa stand?

20. Who were the enemy of the *Men from UNCLE*?

General Knowledge 15

1. What was the surname of the character played by Jodie Foster in *Silence Of The Lambs*?

2. In which 70s TV series did Adam Faith play Ronald Bird?

3. In what year was Nelson Mandela released?

4. How was the Democratic Republic of Congo formerly known?

5. What was the name of the British journalist held hostage in Lebanon for 5 years and released in 1991?

6. Who opened his circus 'The Greatest Show on Earth' in Brooklyn in 1871?

7. Red Vineyard at Arles was the only painting sold in his lifetime by which artist?

8. Which explorer took 24 years to get from Italy to China and back again?

9. What was the name of Morticia Addams' husband in the *Addams Family*?

10. Banquo is a ghost who haunts which Shakespeare character?

11. The twigs of which tree are used to make witches brooms?

12. Who wrote *The Prime of Miss Jean Brodie*?

13. In which soap is Rosamund Street often referred to?

14. Which percussion musical instrument is named after the Spanish word for coconuts?

15. Who composed the *Nutcracker Suite*?

16. How many children were in the *Waltons* family?

17. Which Italian club is known as the Grand Old Lady of Europe?

18. Which British comedienne was the voice of the Fairy Godmother in *Shrek 2*?

19. Which company makes Fairy Liquid?

20. How many contestants start the show in *The Weakest Link*?

"It's a bulllllseye! And here's your host - Jiiiim Bowen!"

General Knowledge 16

1. Which 80s TV series featured the sheriff Roscoe Coltrane?

2. In *Starsky & Hutch*, what was Hutch's first name?

3. Who was elected leader of the Conservative Party in July 1965?

4. What colour shoes does Bart Simpson wear?

5. What colour dress does Wilma Flintstone wear?

6. Grampus Eight are a popular football team in which country?

7. Who committed the first murder in the Bible?

8. Of the British horse racing classics, which one has been competed for the longest?

9. In which TV series would you find the Dowager Countess of Grantham?

10. The novel *The Day of the Jackal* concerns an assassination attempt on which political figure?

11. How many letters of the alphabet are used as Roman numerals?

12. What was the name of the Russian goldsmith famous for his decorative eggs?

13. Which American singer said 'You're not drunk if you can lie on the floor without holding on'?

14. Which comedian used to end his show with 'Goodnight and may your God go with you'?

15. Who did Tim McInnerny play in *Blackadder Goes Forth*?

16. In which film did Veruca Salt sing *I Want It Now*?

17. What is the maximum possible score in 10 Pin Bowling?

18. What was the original name of the Home Guard during WW2?

19. What was the first ocean liner to have a swimming pool?

20. How many times has Tom Cruise been married?

"Stay out of the black and into the red, nothing in this game for two in a bed."

General Knowledge 17

1. Whose beauty products does Cheryl advertise?

2. In which TV series did William Shatner star as veteran police sergeant?

3. Which British TV series stars Emilia Fox as a forensic scientist?

4. The serial killer John George Haigh disposed of the victims by using what substance?

5. In what year was Lord Lucan declared dead?

6. What was the nickname of the American killer Albert Desalvo?

"Look at what you could have won."

7. *Black Night* was the first hit for which colourful rock group?

8. Which bird was Fleetwood Mac's only number one UK hit?

9. Which singer had 38 hit singles before his first solo number one with *Sacrifice* in 1990?

10. Who was lead singer of The Jam?

11. In which sport would you find Michaela Tabb refereeing?

12. Susan Brown was the first woman to compete in which annual event?

13. Which sport features a special event known as the Puissance?

14. What nationality is the F1 driver Felipe Massa?

15. What is Ken Jennings famous for winning?

16. Which Italian patriot gave his name to a type of biscuit?

17. If the first little piggy went to market, where did the second little piggy go?

18. Spiro Agnew was vice president to which American president?

19. Which soldier led a military coup in Uganda in 1971?

20. Which famous explorer was beheaded in 1618?

General Knowledge 18

1 Who played Elsie Tanner in *Coronation Street*?

2 Gertrude Schilling was a famous designer of what ladies fashion items?

3 What was the name of Frank Spencer's daughter in *Some Mothers Do 'Ave 'Em*?

4 Which comedy character asked her friend Madge Allsop to be bridesmaid at her wedding?

5 Who wrote the novel *Our Mutual Friend*?

6 *With a Little Help From My Friends* was the first number one for which group?

7 Which Formula 1 motor racing driver won the *BBC Sports Personality of the Year* in 1994?

8 Which horse prevented Red Rum winning three nationals in a row in 1975?

9 Which player was the first to break Fred Perry's record of three consecutive Wimbledon Singles Titles?

10 Who created *The Liver Birds*?

"And Bully's Special Priiiiize..."

11 In the nursery rhyme *This Little Piggy*, what did the third little piggy have?

12 If something is stannic, which metal does it contain?

13 Which sport did Alan Shephard play on the moon?

14 Idris the Dragon appears in which children's TV programme?

15 Which woodwind instrument is used to represent the bird in Prokofiev's *Peter and The Wolf*?

16 Pulmonary relates to which part of the human body?

17 Lacrimal fluid lubricates which part of the human body?

18 Which bandleader was known as the King of Swing?

19 For what reason did Marlon Brando refuse an Oscar for *The Godfather*?

20 Which two Welsh Rugby Union teams joined forces to become the Ospreys?

General Knowledge 19

1. Who wrote Lady Chatterley's Lover?

2. 1986 was the 900th anniversary of the publication of which famous book?

3. Which Peter was William Hague's Deputy as Leader of the Conservative Party?

4. At which winter sports resort is the Cresta Run?

5. What is the male part of a flower called?

6. What is the collective name for Torquay, Brixham and Paignton?

7. Who said 'In the future everyone will be world famous for 15 minutes'?

8. With which disaster would you associate Molly Brown?

9. According to the World Association of Newspapers, which country has the 3 biggest circulation papers in the world?

10. Why is The Sun often boycotted in Liverpool?

11. Who was Editor of The Sun from 1981 to 1994?

"Now the cash you won for charity earlier... that's safe."

12. Which full colour newspaper was launched in 1986?

13. Who was the first woman Editor of a UK National Newspaper?

14. What is reputed to have been invented by Ray Tomlinson?

15. Who invented the clockwork radio?

16. Which American inventor is often mistakenly credited with inventing peanut butter?

17. Who invented the television?

18. Which lady was the first recipient of a patent for a modern bra?

19. Thomas Crapper and Sons are associated with which invention?

20. Rickenbacker made which musical invention?

Geography 1

1. The island of Bora Bora is administered by what country?

2. What is the largest island in Canada?

3. What line on a map connects places of equal rainfall?

4. How many miles from London to the Falkland Islands?

5. In which country would you find the longest covered bridge in the world?

6. What is the largest city in Dalmatia?

7. The name of what sea means *The Middle of the Earth*?

8. What name is given to the deepest part of the Mediterranean Sea?

9. Where would you find the Great Bitter Lake?

10. Which country's capital city lies on the River Aare?

11. Where is the Barbary Coast?

12. What Swiss city is located 62 kilometres northeast of Geneva?

13. What four countries make up the UK?

14. Which country has the largest population?

15. Which country has the longest coastline?

16. What is the highest mountain in South Africa?

17. What is the largest city in the Arctic Circle?

18. Muscat is the capital city of which country?

19. What straits connect the Persian Gulf with the Arabian Sea?

20. The Angel Falls are part of what river?

"Super, smashing, great."

Geography 2

1. What collective name is sometimes used to refer to Belgium and the Netherlands?

2. Which country is Majorca a part of?

3. What is the highest mountain in Western Europe?

4. How is Pleasant Island now known?

5. Where would you find the Jutland Peninsula?

"Innnnnn four..."

6. In which Spanish region is the city of Santiago de Compostela located?

7. The Swiss town of Meyrin is the closest settlement to what location?

8. What are states of Switzerland called?

9. The summit of Everest runs across the border of which two countries?

10. In which country can the largest ancient Pyramid be found?

11. The Duchy of Nassau is now part of what country?

12. In what country can the region of Zeeland be found?

13. What city is the capital of Qatar?

14. What is the largest country of South America?

15. What is one of the smallest countries of South America?

16. How is the Southern tip of South America known?

17. On a map, the vertical lines are called what?

18. What is the smallest country on mainland Africa?

19. What P is a sparsely populated region located at the southern end of South America?

20. To which South American country does Easter Island belong?

History 1

1. At *The Boston Tea Party* how did the demonstrators disguise themselves?

2. What was the original name of the City of Alexandria before it was renamed by Alexander the Great?

3. What name was given to signatories of the Sanquhar Declaration?

4. Which Private Company ruled India for 100 years?

5. Who was the headmaster of Rugby School from 1828 to 1841?

6. What name was given to the continuation of the Roman Empire in the East?

7. Where did Charles I hide after the Battle of Naseby?

8. What name was given to the Kings of Egypt?

9. What war resulted in the ceding of Hong Kong to the British?

"You win nothing but your BFH... Bus Fare Home"

10. What famous palace was built for Cardinal Thomas Wolsey before being seized by Henry VIII?

11. What was the last Muslim city in Spain?

12. Who was the first Sultan of Egypt and Syria?

13. How did Mata Hari die?

14. In what year were Scotland and England unified?

15. Where would an Anchorite live?

16. In what year was the Magna Carta signed?

17. Which Chairman of British Rail axed over 4000 miles of routes?

18. With what type of buildings is Sir George Gilbert Scott most associated with?

19. With what type of buildings are The Stevensons, a family of Engineers, most associated?

20. Which city is the burial place of Richard III?

History 2

1. What language was the Magna Carta written in?

2. Who was Consort of King James I and VI?

3. What ship is most closely associated with Captain Cook?

4. The Carronade was one of the last cannons used by the Royal Navy in the 1800s. In which town were Carronade's made?

5. In what year did construction of the Berlin Wall begin?

6. Who was the leader of Polish political party Solidarity?

7. The President and many of the leaders of which country died in a plane crash in 2010?

8. Constantine I ruled which country in the 9th Century?

9. Who was the leader of the FBU during the UK firefighter dispute 2002–2003?

10. With what events is the name Robert Catesby most associated?

11. Where did the Boxer Rebellion take place?

12. How long did the General Strike last?

13. What was General Franco's Christian name?

"101 or more with 6 darts for tonight's mystery star prize"

14. In what year did Queen Victoria celebrate her Diamond Jubilee?

15. Which Pretender to the English throne was pardoned and thereafter employed in the Royal kitchens as a servant?

16. Who was the last English monarch to win his throne on the field of Battle?

17. A major flood killed over 2000 people in Holland, England and Scotland in which year of the 20th Century?

18. Who succeeded Kruschev as leader of the Soviet Union?

19. For what crime was Susan B. Anthony arrested in 1872?

20. Who founded Pennsylvania?

History 3

1. From which house was Edward III of England a part?

2. Who was Mary Queen of Scots' first husband?

3. What papal name was taken by Roderic Borgia?

4. What city had the first ghetto?

"All for the throw of a dart"

5. What was the name of Lord Nelson's daughter by Lady Hamilton?

6. What name was given to the brash young women in short skirts of the 1920s?

7. What year was 'The Prague Spring'?

8. In what year did women's franchise become equal to men's in the UK?

9. In what year did the Great Wall Street Crash take place?

10. In what year did the Dot Com Bubble burst?

11. Who developed the concept of horsepower?

12. What globally important revolution started around 1760?

13. Which two countries came together in the Anschluss of 1938?

14. What Kingdom of the 1800s included parts of present-day Germany, Poland, Russia, Lithuania, Denmark, Belgium and the Czech Republic?

15. The Velvet Revolution saw which country split apart?

16. How did the Romans refer to Ireland?

17. By crossing what river did Julius Caesar threaten the Roman Republic?

18. What was Rasputin's first name?

19. Who was the first British monarch to set foot in Spain?

20. Who was the Captain of the Titanic?

History 4

1. What is the name of Winston Churchill's Kent home?

2. What was Gandhi's first name?

3. Who shot Archduke Ferdinand?

4. In which city was Robert Kennedy assassinated?

"Go for your lights"

5. Who is probably the most famous person to have been born in Sirte, Syria?

6. In the War of the Roses, what colour of Rose represented Yorkshire?

7. Who discovered the anaesthetic properties of chloroform?

8. Which Roman Road ran from London to York?

9. Which US President created the first National Park?

10. Which President's first lady was called Lady Bird?

11. Which American President was born in Plains, Georgia?

12. What does Jimmy Carter admit to seeing, that no other American President has admitted to?

13. What are the names of Barack Obama's two daughters?

14. Which US President was assassinated in 1881?

15. Which President oversaw the purchase of Alaska from Russia?

16. Which countries contested The Winter War?

17. In what year did Sir Edmund Hillary first scale Everest?

18. In what year was the Empire State Building finished?

19. In what year was the book *1984* published?

20. In what year did the Great Train Robbery take place?

Horse racing

1. What is reckoned to be the richest horse race in the world?

2. Which premier racetrack opened in March 2010?

3. Where is The Derby usually held?

4. How is Michelle Payne famous in the world of Horse Racing?

5. Which horse holds the record for the fastest speed in the Kentucky Derby?

6. How many times was Gordon Richards the Champion Jockey?

7. What change was made to the Cheltenham Festival in 2005?

8. How many furlongs in a mile?

9. What age was Lester Piggott when he retired?

10. What is the highest fence in the Grand National?

11. How is Rupert Walsh better know?

12. Who rode Shergar to victory in the 1981 Derby?

13. Which top jockey was born in Stirling in 1942?

14. What is the top racecourse in Hong Kong called?

15. Who released the book *Winner: A Racing Life* shortly after his retirement in 2015?

16. The world's largest thoroughbred racehorse stud is located in Ireland. What is it called?

17. What is the name of the Maktoum family's private thoroughbred horse racing stable?

18. What organisation owns 15 British Racecourses?

19. Near which town is the national stud located?

20. What is the most valuable jump race in Europe?

"You've got the time it takes for the board to revolve..."

How Many?

1. How many acres in a square mile?

2. How many countries are there in the world today?

3. How many days in a leap year?

4. How many Cinque Ports were there originally?

5. How many bits in a byte?

6. How many weeks are in a year?

7. How many Oscars did John Wayne win?

8. How many miles is it from London to Paris?

9. How many horses have won The Derby twice?

10. How many valves in the human heart?

11. How many legs does a spider have?

12. How many teams are there in the English Football Premier League?

13. How many books were in *The Hitchikers Guide to the Galaxy*?

14. How many buildings collapsed during the 9/11 terror attacks on New York?

15. How many people have walked on the moon?

16. How many weeks did *Love Is All Around* by Wet Wet Wet stay at No. 1?

17. How many days should a quarantine period traditionally last?

18. How many gallons in a firkin?

19. How many books are in *the Bible*?

20. How many *Police Academy* films were made?

"Remember, you can't beat a bit of Bully!"

In the News

1. Who was President of Venezuela from 1999 to 2013?

2. Prince Andrew's friendship with whom caused him to make an official announcement in 2015?

3. Who caused ire by verbally attacking the audience in a 2015 General Election Leader debate?

4. Who was the leader of Plaid Cymru at the 2015 General Election?

5. Who won the 2014 Costa Book Award for *H is for Hawk*?

6. What nickname was given to Mohammed Emwazi in 2015?

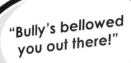

"Bully's bellowed you out there!"

7. What was the maiden name of Andy Murray's wife?

8. How many seats of the 59 competed for did the Scottish National Party win at the 2015 General Election?

9. To the nearest million, what was the population of the UK calculated at in 2014?

10. What name was given to the scam where gangs would deliberately cause accidents in order to submit inflated insurance claims?

11. What did the London Borough of Lambeth ban in 2015?

12. Who became Jeremy Corbyn's deputy in 2015?

13. Who was the last British resident to be detained in Guantanamo Bay?

14. Which Conservative minister stood down in November 2015 due to allegations of bullying?

15. What nickname is often given to the migrant camp near Calais?

16. The *Top Gear* crew caused controversy by filming stunts where in March 2016?

17. In early 2016, which company was in dispute with the FBI over granting access to an alleged terrorist's phone?

18. Which band was playing at the Bataclan Theatre during the Paris terror attacks of 2015?

19. In 2002, which Swede was at the head of the Inspectors looking for Nuclear weapons in Iraq?

20. What was Eva Carneiro's job until late 2015?

In What Year?

1. In what year were the first Modern Olympics held?

2. In what year did the UK TV Series *I'm A Celebrity... Get Me Out of Here* begin?

3. In what year was Peter Sutcliffe finally arrested?

4. In what year did the Blitz begin?

5. In what year was Miley Cyrus born?

6. In what year was Tony Blair elected Prime Minister?

7. In what year were the Olympics last held in London?

8. In what year did Prince release *1999*?

9. In what year did Prince William marry Kate Middleton?

10. In what year did South Sudan become an independent country?

11. In what year did Charles de Gaulle die?

12. In what year was the smoking ban introduced in England?

13. In what year did Blackburn Rovers win the English Premiership?

14. In what year did Jim Henson die?

15. In what year did Helen Sharman travel into space?

16. In what year was The Battle of Bannockburn?

17. In what year did Heathrow Airport open?

18. In what year did Saddam Hussein become leader of Iraq?

19. In what year was Sky TV launched?

20. In what year did Mohamed Al Fayed buy Harrods?

"101 or more with 6 darts for tonight's mystery star prize"

Inventions

1. With whom did Thomas Edison fight the *War of Currents*?

2. Beto Perez gave us which dancing/ fitness craze?

3. The Scottish Maiden was an early form of what device?

4. Which man, born in 1910, is regarded as one of the most famous French Inventors?

5. Eugene Polley gave us which time saving invention?

6. Mike Nesmith, of The Monkees, was the son of the inventor of which office item?

7. Which Swiss designer created the univers typeface?

8. It is said that high heels were first worn at whose wedding in 1533?

9. Levi Strauss is associated with the invention of which garment?

10. Who invented logarithms?

"Let's check that with Bully"

11. Markus Persson gave us which worldwide gaming sensation?

12. Pietro Ferrero invented which spreadable food?

13. Who invented the machine used to resurface ice rinks?

14. Garrett Brown invented what type of film camera, allowing very smooth motion shots?

15. What did Henry F. Phillips introduce for carpenters?

16. Who is credited with inventing the seatbelt?

17. What did George de Mestral invent?

18. Who invented the Bouncing Bomb?

19. Who invented the V-2 rocket for Nazi Germany?

20. Which family invented the whirlpool bath?

Ireland

1. What city on the South West of Ireland is believed to be the oldest city on the island?

2. What is the largest county in Ireland by area?

3. Which Irish city is associated with the production of fine crystal?

4. Which Englishman led Ireland to their first ever Football World Cup?

5. In which county of Ireland would you find the Twelve Bens mountain range?

6. What 'is worth seeing but not worth going to see'?

7. What town was the birthplace of Liam Neeson and Ian Paisley?

8. In what year did the Battle of the Boyne take place?

9. In which Irish town was Bram Stoker born?

10. Who was the founder of the O'Brien dynasty?

11. What is the most populous province of Ireland?

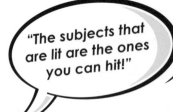

"The subjects that are lit are the ones you can hit!"

12. What name was given to the part of Ireland directly governed by England in the Middle Ages?

13. Naas is the county town of which Irish county?

14. What river runs through Dublin?

15. In which county of Ireland can the highest peak be found?

16. What is the premier University in Belfast?

17. What does the prefix Bally mean in Irish place names?

18. Whose name has been added to Belfast City Airport?

19. In which Northern Irish county is the town of Dungannon?

20. In what city did Bloody Sunday take place?

Italy

1. What city is the capital of Sardinia?

2. What is Italian for Dad?

3. Which Italian city, often regarded as the richest, shares the same flag as England?

4. What was the name of the Italian Ruling house after unification?

5. In what year did Michelangelo finish painting the ceiling of the Sistine Chapel?

6. What year as seen as the end of the period of Italian unification?

7. What is Rome's nickname?

8. What group name was given to Italian Protestants?

9. How many countries does Italy border?

10. What is the 'second city' of Italy?

"Bully's bellowed you out there!"

11. Who was the leader of Forza Italia from 1994 to 2009?

12. In what Italian city did the murder of Meredith Kercher take place?

13. What is the unofficial national animal of Italy?

14. What are the two independent states fully within the borders of Italy?

15. In Italy what are Etna, Stromboli, and Vesuvius?

16. What is the most common surname in Italy?

17. Who is the patron Saint of Venice?

18. In what Italian city would you find the Veiled Christ?

19. The name of what former Italian coin derives from the Latin for Shield?

20. Rome's busiest airport is named after whom?

Jobs

1. What B would cut your hair?

2. Which E might rewire your house?

3. What W could bring you your meal at a restaurant?

4. Which F might rescue a cat from a tree?

5. Which D would help you look after your teeth?

6. Which D delivers beer to pubs?

7. Which B is in charge of the dining room in a mansion?

8. Which C could make you a barrel?

9. Which P may treat your ankle?

10. Which P may make sure that your movie plays correctly in the cinema?

11. Which O works on behalf of the public to investigate complaints?

12. Which S may write the script for a film?

13. Which P has the job of generating buzz for a celebrity?

14. Which C might design a sequence of dances?

15. Which S would transcribe a court hearing?

16. Which G acts as an attendant to a hunting expedition?

17. What C spins a roulette wheel?

18. What S is a specialist in wine?

19. What C could be found selling fruit at a London market?

20. What M attempts to contact the dead?

"You've had a good night out - but you go home with nowt!"

Let's Get Quizzy! 1

1. What is the name of *Danger Mouse*'s sidekick?

2. What is the name of the Yellow Bulldog Pup in *Paw Patrol*?

3. What cartoon baddies name is a play on Cruel Devil?

"Throwers and Knowers"

4. What colour is *Thomas the Tank Engine*?

5. Who was the original presenter of *Gladiators* alongside Ulrika Jonsson?

6. The Duchy of Cornwall is one of two royal duchies in England, can you name the other?

7. What name is given to the keyboard that has the letters arranged based on how often they are used, for example, the most common letters are in the centre row of keys, so less hand movement is required?

8. In the quiz show *Deal or No Deal*, how many sealed boxes are there?

9. What name is given to a crime, involving unjustified threats to make a gain or cause loss to another unless a demand is met?

10. In the play *Amadeus*, who claims to have poisoned Mozart?

11. What is Mike's surname in *Charlie and the Chocolate Factory*?

12. What name was given to the colonisation of Ulster by King James VI and I?

13. Where can you find the only major sea cliffs between Wales and Scotland?

14. Which bell is synonymous with the name of Lloyd's of London?

15. Which television drama series features the trial of Joe Miller and the reopening of the Sandbrook case?

16. As of 2014, what is American Bill de Blasio's job?

17. What city is the filming site for the fictional city of King's Landing in *Game of Thrones*?

18. Who helps her comedy partner Mel present *The Great British Bake Off*?

19. Which online news aggregator and blog was launched in May 2005?

20. Which pub chain announced they would no longer be serving Sunday roasts?

Let's Get Quizzy! 2

1. What is the name of the premier Welsh Language TV station?

2. What Roman Road ran roughly from Canterbury to Wroxeter?

3. Which athletic shoe and clothing manufacturer's logo is called the 'swoosh'?

4. Clint Eastwood was mayor of which Californian town?

5. Which African city means 'victorious' in Arabic?

6. Which company is the largest chocolate manufacturer in North America?

7. Who was Chancellor of Germany from 1998 to 2005?

8. What company has Natasha Kaplinsky worked for since 2011?

9. Who did Bruce Jenner become?

10. Gertrude Ederle was the first woman to do what in 1926?

"Look at what you could have won."

11. Which Premier League football team is nicknamed the Cherries?

12. What is the common name given to a remote detachment of Edwards Air Force Base in Nevada, which is the frequent subject of conspiracy theories?

13. Queen Maud Land, a region of Antarctica, is a dependent territory of which country?

14. What was the world's first officially perforated postage stamp?

15. What colour is Gonzo in *The Muppets*?

16. What is the name of the Killer in *Pyscho*?

17. Which supposed messiah died at the age of 33 in 1993?

18. Which month represents the letter N in the Phonetic Alphabet?

19. What name is given to the reputed lake monster living in Lake Champlain, in North America?

20. For how many years was John Major Prime Minister?

Let's Get Quizzy! 3

1. What is the real name of Jimmy Krankie?

2. What does JPEG stand for, as in a JPEG file?

3. Which Bush dropped out of the 2016 Presidential Race?

4. Who sang the theme song to the eighties sitcom *A Fine Romance*?

5. Is rhubarb a fruit or a vegetable?

6. In DIY, anaglypta and vymura are both types of what?

7. What was invented for dog training by Francis Galton in 1876?

8. What name was given to a series of American domestic programmes in the thirties in response to the Great Depression?

9. What was the name of Michael Jackson's pet Monkey?

10. RICE is considered a mnemonic for first-aid treatment for soft tissue injuries, the acronym is for Rest, Ice, Compression and what else?

11. Who was Fred Flintstone's wife?

12. Who coined the term The Iron Curtain?

13. Who was Nelson Mandela's wife during his incarceration?

14. Who married Margaret Kempson in 1942 and Margaret Roberts in 1951?

15. Which TV presenter set up the charity Childline in 1986?

16. What word is the exact opposite of nocturnal?

17. What is the most populous city in the far north of Queensland, Australia?

18. Who was Will Carling's first wife?

19. Who was the First Labour Prime Minister?

20. What is the largest inland city of New South Wales, Australia?

"Stay out of the black and into the red, nothing in this game for two in a bed."

Let's Get Quizzy! 4

1. George Melly was associated with what type of music?

2. Where is Jim Morrison buried?

3. In Bodger and Badger, what did Bodger love to eat?

4. Who gave voice to Shrek?

5. If you have otalgia, what are you suffering from?

6. What P is good timekeeping?

"Look at what you could have won."

7. In which quiz were clues identified by Greek letters, which were replaced by hieroglyphs in series 4?

8. Severe flooding allowed hundreds of wild animals to escape from a zoo in which country in June 2015?

9. Ted Danson portrays sheriff Hank Larsson in the second season of which TV show?

10. Who wrote the song You Can Leave Your Hat On?

11. Who was the first non British Manager to win the FA Cup?

12. Bacchus was the Roman god of what?

13. Who links Hi-de-hi with Watership Down?

14. 'So, you are the little woman who wrote the book that started this great war!' - who said this and who was it said to?

15. Phillip Schofield gained his first broadcasting experience whilst living with his family in which country?

16. What colour is a vivid purplish red colour named after the flower of a plant which took its name from a 16th century German botanist?

17. Which job did John Nott have in the Government during the Falklands War?

18. Actor Robert Redford named which film festival after a Wild West outlaw?

19. What is the official language of the Flemish Community?

20. How heavy in kilograms is a metre cubed of water?

Let's Get Quizzy! 5

1. *The Dogs of War* is a novel by which thriller writer?

2. What was the last name of Rachel in the American sitcom *Friends*?

3. Who owns the television production company called Harpo?

4. Who designed the cenotaph in Whitehall, London?

5. In which residence does the Duke of Northumberland live?

6. What is the name of Tranmere's ground?

"And Bully's Special Priiiiize..."

7. Which film director includes a scene featuring a shooting star in a lot of his films?

8. What code word in the phonetic alphabet is also the name of a capital city?

9. Which small peninsula crossing the mouth of Poole Harbour is well known for its high property values?

10. Who did Ringo Starr marry in 1981?

11. The name of which wine glass is also a musical instrument?

12. Who wrote *Cinderella*, *Little Red Riding Hood*, *Puss in Boots* and *The Sleeping Beauty*?

13. Who was Jim Callaghan's wife?

14. In London, apart from being Royalty, what connects Her Majesty, Prince Edward, the Duke of York & the Prince of Wales?

15. Which hostess from *The Price is Right* married John Major's son?

16. Who played Christopher Foyle in the long-running series *Foyle's War*?

17. Who was the first player to be Footballer of the Year in both England and Scotland?

18. What was the name of the twins who assisted Pat Sharp on *Fun House*?

19. In Roman Times, what was a Gladius?

20. Name the most widely spoken constructed language in the world?

Let's Get Quizzy! 6

1. Nuuk is the capital of which island?

2. Name the most populated city in Brazil?

3. Neuquén is the largest city of which South American region?

4. Which American city has the largest Chinese population outside Asia?

5. What does CAMRA campaign for?

6. What number is 5pm on the 24hr clock?

7. Who was the original 'It' girl?

8. What was the highest grossing film in the UK until it was outsold by Titanic?

9. What is the name of the art of trimming trees and shrubs into ornamental shapes?

10. Who was the first President of France to be elected by a direct popular vote?

11. Who published the 'Dynamic Tension' course?

12. Which Scottish castle was the birth place of Princess Margaret in 1930?

13. In 2012, who resigned as Conservative MP for Corby to spend more time with her family in New York City?

14. Which Lincolnshire town hosted the largest fishing fleet in the world by the mid-twentieth century?

15. Who invented the reflective road stud or cat's eye in 1934?

16. Which former *Corrie* star topped FHM's list of the world's sexiest woman in 2015?

17. As of March 2015, which professional networking website reported more than 364 million acquired users?

18. What did Edward Chad Varah found in 1953?

19. Who had a hit with the song *Kids in America* in 1981?

20. Which President of South Africa released Nelson Mandela?

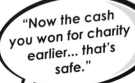

"Now the cash you won for charity earlier... that's safe."

Let's Get Quizzy! 7

1. Who is best known for his book *Les Propheties*?

2. UPS are one of the world's biggest delivery companies – what does UPS stand for?

3. The traditional dancing of which country featured in *Riverdance*?

4. Which Chinese city has the world's busiest container port?

5. What is mozzarella cheese made from?

6. What is the name of a large linear earthwork that roughly follows the current border between England and Wales?

7. Name the metabolic process that converts sugar to acids or alcohol?

8. In which English County did John Constable do much of his painting?

9. Parcheesi is the American name for the children's board game we call what?

10. What was Lloyd Grossman's catchphrase on *Through the Keyhole*?

11. In which Ian Fleming novel does the dog Edison feature?

12. Which world known figure died just five days after Princess Diana?

13. What term is often used to describe areas of the World which have a greater than average number of centenarians?

14. What is the fourth oldest university in the English-speaking world?

15. Who was located in Abbottabad?

16. What is President Barack Obama's middle name?

17. It was once thought that a giraffe was a cross between which two animals?

18. Auric was the first name of which Bond villain?

19. Who is Tim Lovejoy's TV partner?

20. What are digital socks?

"Super, smashing, great."

Let's Get Quizzy! 8

1. In what country was James Watt born?

2. In which town did the *Flintstones* live?

3. What city was once the capital of the maritime Republic of Ragusa?

4. The mongrel Pickles became famous in 1966 for finding what?

5. What would you add to a pizza to make it a Pizza Crunch?

6. Name the national flag carrier airline of the Netherlands?

7. Which Peter is the most prominent TV voice artist in the world today?

8. What board game name comes from the Latin, 'I play'?

9. Which British company is the second-largest retailer in the world measured by revenues?

10. As of 2015, how many MEPs are there in the European Parliament?

11. In which country was Roald Dahl born?

12. Which game takes its name from the Chinese word for sparrow?

13. Which former *Strictly Come Dancing* star is now a top Life Coach?

14. Which actor played the lead role in the eighties ITV drama *The Charmer*?

15. Which English Cricketer of the 2000s was nicknamed Freddie?

16. Who donated his own prepared tomb for the burial of Jesus?

17. What is the most famous bridge in Prague?

18. What does the 'E' stand for in the equation 'E equals M C squared'?

19. Who presents *Deal or No Deal*?

20. In pop music, whose 1986 album was entitled *Graceland*?

"Innnnnn five..."

Let's Get Quizzy! 9

1. Who married Slovenian model Melania Knauss in 2005?

2. What would your hobby be if you used slip?

3. What is the motto of Harvard University?

4. In which city were the 2010 Winter Olympics based?

5. Leonardo Da Vinci International Airport serves which Italian city?

6. Which 90s American sitcom starred John Lithgow and Joseph Gordon-Levitt?

7. What are Dreamies?

8. Which British glossy magazine is targeted at those interested in society events?

9. Coulrophobia is the fear of what type of entertainers?

10. Who gave us the 'quick reminders' on *Blind Date*?

11. What everyday product comes from the Aztec word for 'bitter water'?

12. Which famous person was born Erik Weisz?

13. What are the six colours on a Rubik's cube?

14. Who was the male star of *Cutthroat Island* alongside Geena Davis?

15. Where did Magnum solve his crimes?

16. A dolorimeter is an instrument used to measure what?

17. Who took over leadership of al-Qaeda after the death of Osama Bin Laden?

18. What letter is represented in Morse code by a single dot?

19. Who was the third President of the United States?

20. What type of transport was SRN1 first made in 1959?

"You win nothing but your BFH... Bus Fare Home"

Let's Get Quizzy! 10

1. Which Brazilian city is the largest in the Southern Hemisphere?

2. In which century was Harvard University established?

3. As of 2015, what is the minimum age you have to be to open a Facebook account?

4. How many red stripes are there on the American flag?

5. How much was a dog license to buy in 1987 (the year it was abolished)?

6. In fashion, what kind of garment is a baldric?

7. Who sang *Three Steps to Heaven* in 1975?

8. What percentage is usually paid as a tithe?

"101 or more with 6 darts for tonight's mystery star prize"

9. Which Grand Prix circuit is only 1.95 miles long?

10. What colour is the Duracell bunny?

11. Kevin Ashman is a member of which TV Quiz team?

12. Where are shipbuilders Cammell Laird based?

13. What was the job of Sting's character in *Quadrophenia*?

14. What was Linda Ronstadt's biggest UK hit?

15. Who served as Leader of the Labour Party from July 1992 until his death from a heart attack in May 1994?

16. Singer Louisa Rose Allen is better known by what stage name?

17. Where on the West Coast of England does the Coast to Coast walk traditionally begin?

18. What rank of nobility comes between Earl and Baron?

19. What name is usually given to the pantomime dame in *Aladdin*?

20. Who wrote *Islands in the Stream*?

Let's Get Quizzy! 11

1. Which child film star of the 30s went on to become an American Ambassador in the 80s & 90s?

2. Which British Regiment opened fire on Bloody Sunday?

3. How did John Denver die?

4. Which Scottish company make Teacakes and Caramel Wafers?

5. What four letter word is a state of unconsciousness in which a person: cannot be awakened?

6. On the Faroe Islands, a favourite dish is which seabird stuffed with rhubarb?

7. In what decade was Lorraine Kelly born?

8. Who is the youngest-ever Chief Scout in the UK?

9. What is longer, a mile or a nautical mile?

10. What is the most north-easterly county in Wales?

"All for the throw of a dart"

11. Which state borders California to the north?

12. Who directed *Eraserhead*?

13. What two word phrase refers to any vehicles that move on a railway?

14. Who released an autobiography titled *Voice of an Angel* at 14?

15. In which country was Charles Atlas born?

16. Miles Anderson was the first man to play what role?

17. Who was the Lead Singer of Madness?

18. Which king married Caroline of Anspach?

19. Who was a great-granddaughter of the Emperor Augustus and mother of the Emperor Nero?

20. What is the literal Latin meaning of trivia?

Let's Get Quizzy! 12

1. In Greek Mythology who was the Titan god of endurance and astronomy?

2. Who was the first person to swim the channel?

3. Who is American actress Kate Capshaw married to?

4. Who hosted *This is Your Life* after the death of Eamonn Andrews?

5. What is the name of Harlequins FC ground?

6. On a computer keyboard what letter is directly to the right of 'O'?

7. In Eastenders, what is the name of Stacey Slater's son?

8. Who wrote *Trainspotting*?

9. What were introduced by Chancellor Harold Macmillan on 1956 as a means of encouraging people to save?

10. What was Walt Disney's middle name?

11. Where did *Roger Rabbit* live?

12. Outside London what is Britain's most visited zoo?

"Go for your lights"

13. Who was the first man to win *Strictly Come Dancing*?

14. Which London bridge crossing the River Thames is located between Blackfriars Bridge and Hungerford Bridge?

15. In England and Wales, what is the last public holiday of the calendar year?

16. Which English county would you most associate with TV chef Rick Stein?

17. Butch Cassidy briefly worked in what type of shop in Wyoming?

18. In nature, cocksfoot and Yorkshire fog are types of which plant?

19. His firstname is Steffano and he is an Italian fashion designer born in 1962; what is his lastname?

20. The chonmage is a traditional haircut worn by men in which country?

Let's Get Quizzy! 13

1. With which rugby club did Will Carling play all of his professional career?

2. What is the most common symbol used to represent Presbyterian Churches?

3. What was the tallest building in the world from 1311 to 1549?

4. Who was *Goldfinger*'s henchman?

"You've got the time it takes for the board to revolve..."

5. What nationality was the composer and band leader James Last?

6. What was Will Somer's job at the court of Henry VIII?

7. The name of what vegetable is whispered by actors to make it appear as if they are talking?

8. Whose first business venture was a magazine called *Student*, before setting up a mail-order record business?

9. Thule Air Base, the United States Air Force's most northernmost base, is on which island?

10. Imelda Staunton is married to which *Downton Abbey* actor?

11. Which British retailer was responsible for the creation of the ISBN book catalogue system?

12. Which British spy fled to France to escape prosecution in the late 90s?

13. What breed of dog was Schmeichel, looked after by Chesney in *Coronation Street*?

14. What is film director Wes Anderson's middle name?

15. With which rugby player did Charlotte Church have a relationship?

16. Which street runs between Piccadilly and Oxford Street in the West End of London?

17. How many piers does Blackpool have?

18. What type of bond is a pattern of bricks in a wall in which each course consists of alternate headers and stretchers?

19. Sledging is a term used in which sport to describe insulting or verbally intimidating the opposing player?

20. In what year was the 999 emergency service introduced in the UK?

Let's Get Quizzy! 14

1. In which town does Rick Stein own four restaurants?

2. Who was the host of *Night Fever* on Channel Five?

3. Who wrote the novel *Little House on the Prairie*?

4. The Bodleian Library is in which city?

5. Who founded the Veritas Party?

"Look at what you could have won."

6. Where in the North East of England would you find an extremely important herd of rare White Cattle?

7. James Lovell was the commander of which ill-fated Apollo moon mission?

8. Who was Princess Diana's boyfriend at the time of her death?

9. Which father and son dance duo were big stars of *Britain's Got Talent Series 3*?

10. What is the most common street name in the UK?

11. Who has been the presenter of more *Strictly Come Dancing* live tour shows than anyone else?

12. Which other famous Italian was born on the day Michelangelo died?

13. In what year did the show *Cheers* begin?

14. Who 'sang' *Girl, I'm Gonna Miss You*?

15. How is Prestbury Park better known?

16. What made more money, the most successful *Twilight* movie, or the most successful *Harry Potter* movie?

17. In which city is Harvard University?

18. In which American state is Yale University?

19. In a pantomime, what name is given to the part of the young male played by a girl in boy's clothes?

20. Overeating in ancient Rome was common – a room called a vomitorium was available for people to purge their stomachs to continue eating – True or false?

Let's Get Quizzy! 15

1. Which Producer gave us Boney M and Milli Vanilli?

2. What is the name of the monster said to inhabit Loch Morar?

3. What does a spermologer collect?

4. How many metres in a kilometre and a half?

5. What make of car was John F Kennedy in when he was assassinated?

"You can't beat a bit of Bully!"

6. What six letter winemaking term means the airspace between the wine and the top of bottle it is in?

7. Who founded Gonzo Journalism?

8. Who played Salieri in the 1984 film *Amadeus*?

9. Which of the following foods were not rationed during the Second World War but rationed afterwards: bread, milk, cheese or eggs?

10. What is the name of Barack Obama's wife?

11. Where was the first Centre Parcs opened in the UK?

12. What nationality was motor racing legend Juan Fangio?

13. What nationality is Jean Marc Bosman, famous for the 'Bosman ruling' affecting football throughout Europe?

14. In which garden in Jerusalem was Jesus arrested?

15. Who was the leader of the Diversity Dance Troupe?

16. Who was the husband of actress Valerie Hobson?

17. In which television series is Beyonce pregnant with Michael Jackson's baby?

18. What is the 4th busiest airport in the UK?

19. With which character would you associate the line *I wish I could fly right up to the sky, but I can't*?

20. What are Heysham 2, Hinkley Point B and Dungeness B?

Let's Get Quizzy! 16

1. What W is 'to gloss over or cover up vices, crimes or scandals or to exonerate by means of a perfunctory investigation or through biased presentation of data'?

2. What was the first name of the Kray twins' mother?

3. In verse, how many stresses are there in a pentameter?

4. What is Bear Grylls' real first name?

5. What is the first name of Bill Clinton's daughter?

6. What sport is Tai Woffinden a Champion in?

7. What is the name of the Caribbean Island owned by Richard Branson?

8. Caitlyn Jenner won an Olympic gold medal in which event?

9. *CHiPs* was a popular TV show in the 70s and 80s. What was it short for?

10. Who created *Riverdance*?

11. How many people sit on a jury in England?

12. In which Welsh county is the town of Rhyl?

13. Who was the original host of *Through the Keyhole*?

14. What is the largest city entirely on the European continent?

15. In what year was Nelson Mandela released from prison?

16. Who was the lead singer of M People?

17. When poet David Dunbar stood for parliament in Dumfries in 1857, what expression did he use to describe the town?

18. What force keeps our feet on the ground?

19. Who did Gonzo portray in *The Muppets Christmas Carol*?

20. What is the longest bridge in the UK?

"Remember, you can't beat a bit of Bully!"

Let's Get Quizzy! 17

1. Which American President's name can be found on the Moon?

2. The musical *Kiss Me Kate* is based on which Shakespeare play?

3. Agliophobia is the fear of what?

4. What name was given to tactical unit of a Roman legion consisting of approximately 480 men?

5. Which trivia quiz game show run from 1971 to 1984 and was hosted by Nicholas Parsons?

6. In which martial art are bamboo swords used?

"Bully's bellowed you out there!"

7. Which sauce is an essential part of an Eggs Benedict?

8. Which London suburb was mentioned in the Madness song *Driving In My Car*?

9. What age was Ronnie Corbett when he died?

10. In what year did 'The Arab Spring' begin?

11. Dame Trott traditionally appears in which pantomime?

12. Jake, Ben & Karen were the three Brockman kids in which BBC comedy?

13. Who invented the hovercraft?

14. Which place is the county town of Kent?

15. Which car manufacturer makes the Duster?

16. Which planet has a solar day of approximately 24 hours and 39 minutes, known as a sol?

17. Which Islamic fundamentalist political movement ran Afghanistan from 1996 to 2001?

18. What is a tidal bore?

19. What TV show is an adaptation of *A Song of Ice and Fire*?

20. What do Edward Koch, David Dinkins and Bill de Blasio all have in common?

Let's Get Quizzy! 18

1. Some people are into DIY. What does this stand for?

2. Who does his best to foil the Road Runner?

3. In which song did John Lennon set out to write the most confusing lyrics he could?

4. Who presented *Fun House*?

5. Which nuts are used in a pesto?

6. On which day of the week does the Queen distribute Maunday Money?

7. Which island off the coast of eastern Canada was first mapped by James Cook?

8. Who in 1961 became the first American to travel into space?

9. Where is Shakespeare buried?

"101 or more with 6 darts for tonight's mystery star prize"

10. With which issue did Denis Thatcher famously disagree with Margaret Thatcher?

11. Who was Judi Dench's husband?

12. What was the name of Winston Churchill's wife?

13. Which toy was invented by George Lerner in 1949 and was the first toy advertised on television?

14. In ancient times, where would you have found the Ishtar Gate?

15. Which British aircraft manufacturer produced the Spitfire?

16. Who directed the film *Psycho*?

17. Where was *This Morning* filmed from 1988 to 1996?

18. Which weapon fires a quarrel?

19. The name of which American state is Spanish for snow covered?

20. Which team has won the English Rugby Premiership the most times?

Let's Get Quizzy! 19

1. According to a 2012 BBC report, McDonald's was the world's second largest private employer, which company was first?

2. Who was the long time host of *Blockbusters*?

3. Where are the headquarters of Whittard of Chelsea?

4. What is the largest island country in the world by the number of islands?

5. What was the name of John Major's wife?

6. In which British city was David Beckham born?

7. Gertie in *E.T.* was played by which actress when she was 5 years old?

8. Which fish is used to make an Arbroath Smokie?

9. What is the English name for the Cote d'Azur?

10. What "G" is a part of a city in which members of a minority group live, especially because of social, legal, or economic pressure?

11. US Police used to use numbers for short cut communication until recently – which 2 numbers meant "OK Message Understood"?

12. Which 1836 battle and siege took place near San Antonio in the USA?

13. Where was the first Butlins holiday camp opened?

14. Who performed *King of Wishful Thinking* on the soundtrack of Pretty Woman?

15. TSS is a potentially fatal illness. What does TSS stand for?

16. Which city, in 2015, staged The Ultimate Fighting Championship between Ronda Rousey and Holly Holm?

17. What 2 word term is often used to describe airlines such as Easyjet and Ryanair?

18. Which country won the first Football World Cup?

19. How many people are on each team in *Only Connect*?

20. Who is Anton du Beke's dance partner?

"Let's check that with Bully"

London

1. What road runs from Marylebone Road to Kings Cross, forming part of the Congestion Charge boundary?

2. In July 2013, which London scheme suffered its first fatality?

3. Where were London's first gas operated traffic lights located in 1868?

4. What is the name of the official London residence of the Archbishop of Canterbury?

5. What lock marks the point where the River Thames becomes tidal?

6. Which island on the Thames was known as a major jazz and blues venue in the 1960s?

7. A statue of whom sits at Charing Cross?

8. The Cenotaph sits in which London Street?

9. In which area of London is the Prospect of Whitby a landmark?

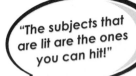

"The subjects that are lit are the ones you can hit!"

10. In which area of London did the first McDonald's open?

11. What does ZSL stand for?

12. What name is given to the point where the North Circular meets the M1?

13. What county was Croydon historically a part of?

14. What nickname has been given to the East London Tech City?

15. What Five Star hotel is found at 68 Regent Street?

16. Where in London is the Golden Gallery?

17. In which area of London do QPR play?

18. What was the tallest building in London until 1962?

19. What area of London lies between Belgravia and the Thames?

20. How is 20 Fenchurch Street, London better known?

Music 1

1. Michael Jackson had only 1 UK top 40 hit in 1991. What was it?

2. What was Michael Jackson's first solo number one in the UK?

3. What was the name of Michael Jackson's ranch?

4. How many times was Michael Jackson married?

5. What was the name of Michael Jackson's tour - cancelled due to his illness and death?

"Go for your lights"

6. Where did Michael Jackson die?

7. What are the names of Michael Jackson's children?

8. Michael Jackson was an honorary Director of which football club?

9. In which 1988 movie did Michael Jackson star?

10. Who was believed to have been the first person to perform the Moonwalk, calling it 'the buzz'?

11. From what album was the song *Billie Jean* taken?

12. Who performed the voiceover in the song *Thriller*?

13. Jackson's scalp was badly burned during the filming of an advert for what product?

14. Michael Jackson was so desperate for what role that he tried to buy the *Marvel Comics* company in the 1980s?

15. Who had a hit with *Vincent*?

16. Who was the lead singer of Tubeway Army?

17. Who 'never promised you a Rose Garden'?

18. Which 70s chart-toppers were formed when *Choice* and *The Golden Hammers* joined up?

19. What was Peter Frampton's biggest UK hit?

20. Who had a massive hit with *Wuthering Heights*?

Music 2

1. Who wrote Chaka Khan's hit *I Feel For You*?

2. Who was the oldest Monkee?

3. For what 1995 hit did Michael and Janet Jackson duet?

4. Who was the manager of The Sex Pistols?

5. Who wrote the song *My Guy*?

6. Which month gave a hit to Earth, Wind and Fire?

7. Who quit The Rolling Stones in 1993?

"You've had a good night out - but you go home with nowt!"

8. Ernest Hogan was a pioneer of what type of music?

9. What song contains the lines: 'Wear a tall hat like a druid in the old days, Wear a tall hat and a tattooed gown'?

10. What type of music blends the sound of Western musical styles such as country with that of rhythm and blues, leading to what is considered "classic" rock and roll?

11. What percussion instrument is made up of two small drums attached to each other?

12. What instrument was famously used for the theme of *The Third Man*?

13. Who wrote the lyrics of *My Way*?

14. Who was the first British female to have five number ones in the UK?

15. Which rapper died on 9th March 1997?

16. Marvin Hamlisch arranged the Ragtime score for which hit 1973 film?

17. Which song begins, 'Our little boy is four years old and quite a little man...'So we spell out the words we don't want him to understand'

18. The saxophone is a member of which family of instruments?

19. What is the largest instrument of the Brass family?

20. What word is the actual title of the 1979 hit typically called *The Pina Colada Song*?

Music 3

1. Brian Jones was a member of what band?

2. What country was the birthplace of Opera?

3. Who had a hit with *Enola Gay*?

4. What was the first ever video on MTV?

"Throwers and Knowers"

5. What note is the highest string of a violin usually tuned to?

6. What instrument is associated with Daniel Barenboim?

7. Who composed *Peter and the Wolf*?

8. Who wrote *You're The Top*?

9. What cover song was Van Halen's first Top 40 hit?

10. Who sang *Lipstick on Your Collar*?

11. What was Chesney Hawkes' major hit?

12. Which British Jazz band had a UK number one in 1961?

13. Who are the two members of The Pet Shop Boys?

14. Who was the leader singer of Garbage?

15. With which band did Boy George achieve his biggest chart successes?

16. What were the first names of the brother and sister in The Carpenters?

17. Who was the lead singer of The Who?

18. Who wrote *Red, Red Wine*?

19. What bands early album titles had a Spanish flair including *Tres Hombres*, *Fandango*, and *Deguello*?

20. Which variations brought lasting fame for Sir Edward Elgar?

Music 4

1. What was the name of *The South Bank Show* theme, composed by Andrew Lloyd Webber?

2. How many members of Destiny's Child were there?

3. In what month of the year did Pilot's *January* hit No. 1?

4. Which band gave us *Black Magic Woman*?

5. Who wrote and arranged most of ELO's hits?

6. Which Italian producer is credited with pioneering Synth Disco?

7. What song contains the line 'It's strange, but it's true, I can't get over the way you love me like you do?'

8. Which twins asked us to *Touch My Bum*?

9. Who is the lead guitarist of Queen?

10. Who were the first band to record *Proud Mary*?

11. Who had a number one single *Ain't No Doubt*?

12. Who is best known as the Drummer of Queen?

13. Which music duo met as children in Queens, New York in 1953?

14. Who is the biggest-selling instrumental musician of the modern era?

15. What charity single featured David Bowie, Elton John, Bono and Heather Small?

16. Which M People song appeared on the soundtrack for *The Full Monty*?

17. Which band was Aston Merrygold a member of?

18. Who sang *Wild Women Do*?

19. Who performed the song *Weird Science* from the film of the same name?

20. What piece of music is the theme to *Just a Minute*?

"Look at what you could have won."

Musicals

1. Which musical features the song *I Know Him So Well*?

2. What musical film starts with '*the Lips*'?

3. *One Night in Bangkok* is a song from what musical?

"And Bully's Special Prize"

4. Which musical includes the song *Leaning on a Lamp post*?

5. In which musical would you find the song *Anything you can do I can do better*?

6. What musical tells the story of a group of impoverished young artists struggling to survive and create a life in New York City's East Village in the thriving days of Bohemian Alphabet City, under the shadow of HIV/AIDS?

7. Which musical tells the story of twins Mickey and Eddie, separated at birth?

8. Who wrote *The Rocky Horror Show*?

9. In what musical does the song *Mr. Cellophane* come from?

10. Which musical does the song *Big Spender* come from?

11. Who made his West End debut playing alongside his mother in *South Pacific*?

12. Who played Dodger in the musical film *Oliver!*?

13. Who has the *New York Times* described as "the most successful, influential and powerful theatrical producer in the world"?

14. Who wrote the music for *West Side Story*?

15. *The Age of Aquarius* is a song from what musical?

16. *Be Prepared* is a song from which 1997 musical? The Lion King

17. What is the longest running Broadway show?

18. The song *Surrey With The Fringe On Top* comes from which musical?

19. *On The Street Where You Live* is a song from which musical?

20. What musical centres on seventeen Broadway dancers auditioning?

Myths and Legends

1. Who was the guardian of Aristotle?

2. What Greek God was depicted in the *Colossus of Rhodes*?

3. Who was a Trojan prince and the greatest fighter for Troy in the Trojan War?

4. Who is the twin Brother of Artemis?

5. What nickname is given to the monster said to inhabit Loch Ness? *Nessie* ✓

6. Which mythical figure is often depicted as a face surrounded by leaves? *The Green Man* ✗

7. Which woods are associated with Robin Hood? *Sherwood Forest* ✓

8. The Paterson-Gimlin film is said to show which mythical beast cross a wooded area? *Bigfoot* ✗

9. In which country is the area of Transylvania?

10. If you are 'Squatching', what are you looking for?

11. According to legend, what happens should the ravens ever leave the Tower of London? *The monarchy will crumble* ✓

12. Who was the Roman Goddess of Agriculture? *Ceres* ✗

13. Where was Arthur taken to recover from his wounds after the Battle of Camlann? *The Lady of the Lake* ✓

14. Who gives King Arthur his sword Excalibur? *Merlin the wizard* ✓

15. Who is the Wizard of Arthurian legend? *Rossleyn Chapel* ✗

16. It is said that part of the cross on which Jesus was hung is buried below which Scottish Church?

17. In Norse mythology, who are the female attendants of Odin? *The Valkriex* ✗

18. Which of the Nine Worlds is home to the Norse Gods? *Asgard* ✗

19. Wednesday is named after what Norse God? *Odin* ✗

20. What species are mingled to produce a Minotaur? *Man and a bull*

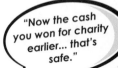

"Now the cash you won for charity earlier... that's safe."

Newspapers

1. How is the 1986 Strike of *News International* workers usually referred to?

2. Who owns the *Daily Star*?

3. What phrase is a generic name used in the United Kingdom for a person, usually with strongly conservative political views, who writes letters to newspapers in a tone of moral outrage?

4. What is the name of the largest paper in Boston, USA?

5. Which weekly newspaper is aimed at those working in the theatre and entertainment?

6. What is the largest newspaper in the United States by circulation?

7. Which Sunday paper is the sister publication to *The Guardian*?

8. How was *The Guardian* known as until 1959?

9. The Barclay Brothers own which major broadsheet?

"Super, smashing, great."

10. Which newspaperman died when he fell from his yacht in 1991?

11. Which national red top ended in 2011?

12. How was *The Daily Mirror* known from 1997 to 2002?

13. What is Ireland's biggest selling Newspaper?

14. What newspaper was launched in early 2016?

15. In newspapers, 'if it bleeds, it...' what?

16. What newspaper is currently edited by Katharine Viner?

17. What is the main local paper in Leicester?

18. Which newspaper gave us *The Broons*?

19. What newspaper has won more Pulitzer prizes than any other News organisation?

20. Which newspaper advertises itself as the Voice of Britain?

Opening Lines

1. Which song starts with 'Start spreading the news'?

2. 'They ask me how I knew, my true love was true' is the first line of which song?

3. Which song does Cher open up with, 'You're struttin' into town like you're slingin' a gun'?

4. What is the first line of *Do They Know It's Christmas*?

5. 'Here I lie, in a lost and lonely part of town' starts which song?

6. What song begins with 'If God had a name, what would it be?'

7. 'I'm so young and you're so old' is the first line of which song?

8. What song begins, 'A-wimoweh, A-wimoweh'?

"101 or more with 6 darts for tonight's mystery star prize"

9. Which folk song begins, 'Speed bonnie boat like a bird on the wing'?

10. The song which begins, 'Every night in my dreams, I see you, I feel you' was a massive hit, what was it?

11. What ABBA song begins, 'I work all night, I work all day, to pay the bills I have to pay'?

12. 'I feel it in my fingers, I feel it in my toes' starts what song?

13. Which 80s classic starts with 'Nobody on the road, nobody on the beach'?

14. What is the first line of *Rock Around The Clock*?

15. Which song begins, 'Ah, look at all the lonely people'?

16. Which numerical song starts 'I was dreaming when I wrote this'?

17. What is the first line of Motorhead's *Ace of Spades*?

18. Who penned the opening line 'there must be some kind of way out of here, said the joker to the thief'?

19. What song begins, 'Don't ask me, what you know is true'?

20. What song begins 'You shake my nerves and you rattle my brain'?

Politics 1

1. What R is a person looking to change social structures through revolutionary means?

2. Are the Conservative Party usually considered to be Right Wing or Left Wing?

3. What political tool involves a symbolic violation of the law?

4. Who preceded John Bercow as Speaker of the House of Commons?

5. Who was Tony Blair's Deputy Prime Minister?

6. Who was Chairman of the Conservative Party from 2012 to 2015?

7. What name is often used to refer to a government minister with no specific responsibilities or a minister who does not head a particular ministry?

8. Who preceded Nigel Farage as leader of UKIP?

9. Who agreed to stand aside to allow the new Prime Minister Alec Douglas-Home the chance to enter the House of Commons?

10. What is the name of the bell rung in Parliament to let people know that a vote is about to commence?

"All for the throw of a dart"

11. What political group did Tommy Robinson form in 2016?

12. What does UKIP stand for?

13. What colour is associated with The Labour Party?

14. Who was the first Labour MP?

15. Who did Russell Brand label 'a pound shop Enoch Powell'?

16. Who led the Labour Party from 1980 to 1983?

17. Which constituency did Tony Benn represent for his last 17 years in office?

18. What University did George Osbourne attend?

19. What was the Conservative Party slogan for the 1979 General Election?

20. What Socialist society was formed in 1884?

Politics 2

1. Who has represented Witney since 2001?

2. What seat was represented by Nye Bevan?

3. In the 80s, where did women set up a blockade protesting against the basing of Cruise Missiles?

4. Who was the Lib Dem candidate for London Mayor in 2004?

5. What seat does George Osbourne represent?

6. What is the religion of Democrat Politician Harry Reid?

7. In what country was Ted Cruz born?

"Go for your lights"

8. Who was the Republican nominee for Vice President in the 1960 Presidential election?

9. Who is the only US President to have resigned?

10. What was the slogan of Nancy Reagan's anti-drug campaign?

11. Who ran against Barrack Obama in the 2012 US Presidential election?

12. Which amendment to the US Constitution gave women the right to vote?

13. Who was George W Bush's Vice President?

14. In US politics, what name is given to the day when the greatest number of US states hold primary elections?

15. What slogan/ Twitter hashtag was used by Bernie Sanders during his 2016 Presidential campaign?

16. How often are general elections in the USA?

17. Who is the longest serving Independent in Congressional history?

18. What name is given a female consort of the President?

19. What title is given to a President once they leave office?

20. Which American transport workers trade union had 1.3 million members in 2013?

Pot Luck 1

1. Which former Monty Python member went *Around the World in 80 Days*?

2. When do you use a snorkel?

3. What nationality is Rock Star Bono?

4. In what decade did The Bee Gees reach number one with *You Win Again*?

5. In which sitcom would you hear about Mrs Slocombe's pussy?

6. How many members of B*Witched were there?

7. Who wrote *Angels and Demons*?

8. In what year did ITV begin?

9. What city is the seat of the European Court of Justice?

"You've got the time it takes for the board to revolve..."

10. What does SCUBA stand for?

11. In the UK, what word is usually used to describe a surface coal quarry?

12. What is Simony?

13. In which Country is the city of Tripoli?

14. Which Python directed *Brazil*?

15. What alternative name for black cumin is also the name of a TV cook?

16. In which cocktail would you find white rum, mint leaves, lime juice, sugar and soda?

17. What is Fred Flintstone's catchphrase?

18. What name do we give to the promotion of fraudulent or ignorant medical practices?

19. What title is given to the Chamberlain of the Pope's household?

20. Which WWE champion was born on 23rd April 1977?

Pot Luck 2

1. What part of a Cockney's body are his plates of meat?

2. Whose real name was Phyllis Pechey?

3. What is a fifth of 300?

4. What crime did Bruce Reynolds mastermind?

5. What seaside resort, with castle, sits roughly halfway between Whitby and Bridlington?

6. What is the capital city of Canada?

7. What material is an Ascot usually made from?

8. Who wrote the 1929 work *A Farewell to Arms*?

9. Who painted the Queen on the occasion of her 80th Birthday?

10. In what country would you find the mouths of the Limpopo river?

11. What were the christian names of *The Golden Girls*?

12. What number is represented by the Roman Numeral V?

13. How is Arthur Wellesley better known?

14. *Shaft* is an African-American Detective in book and film. What is his first name?

15. Which day's child is fair of face?

16. Which Irish singer organised Band Aid?

17. What is the most abundant metal in the earth's crust?

18. In Monopoly how much do you collect when you pass Go?

19. Which Monty Python member gave us *Fawlty Towers*?

20. How many squares on a Rubiks Cube?

"All for the throw of a dart"

Pot Luck 3

1. What would you do with a Magic 8-Ball?

2. What colour is the road Dorothy follows in *The Wizard of Oz*?

3. What was the name of *Doctor Who's* robot dog?

4. How many common parents do full siblings have?

5. From which language does the word typhoon originate?

6. What is the highest hill in Ireland?

7. Who was the Policeman in *'Allo 'Allo*?

8. What number is represented by the Roman Numeral X?

9. What is the main constituent of Kebab meat?

10. What number is represented by the Roman Numeral M?

11. What is the largest Lake in Europe?

12. In what decade was Jeff Lynne of the ELO born?

13. In 1984, the worst famine in history occurred where?

14. Who wrote the play *Long Day's Journey Into Night*?

15. Who had a hit in 1977 with *Exodus*?

16. What is the symbol for the chemical element Potassium?

17. In what fictional country is *The Prisoner of Zenda* set?

18. In which month of the year is the Cheltenham Festival held?

19. Who gave us the Adrian Mole character?

20. Who is the Greek equivalent of Roman God Neptune?

"You can't beat a bit of Bully!"

Pot Luck 4

1. Which writer inspired *The Grand Budapest Hotel*?

2. Who presents *Celebrity Juice*?

3. Which beer used the slogan 'Probably the Best Lager in the World'?

4. What was Joey's surname in *Friends*?

5. Who produced *The Love Boat* and *Dynasty*?

6. In what country was *The Grand Budapest Hotel* filmed?

7. What was Boney M's first UK hit?

8. Who had a hit with *The wind of Change*?

9. Who has been CEO of Channel 4, Chairman of the BBC and Chairman of ITV?

10. What is the common name for the Aurora Borealis?

11. What year saw the beginning of MTV?

12. What number is represented by the Roman Numeral C?

13. Which of the *Teletubbies* was red?

14. What is the longest side of a right angled triangle known as?

15. Who backed Frank Zappa?

16. What is the name of the dragon in *The Hobbit*?

17. What is a vendetta?

18. Who wrote 'Allo 'Allo?

19. Halloumi is a type of cheese originating from which island?

20. How many players in a cricket team?

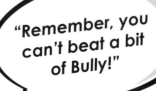

"Remember, you can't beat a bit of Bully!"

Pot Luck 5

1. Tiny Tim appears in which Dickens novel?

2. Who played V in *V for Vendetta*?

3. Who wrote *The Sound of Music*?

4. Who was the only male member of Boney M?

5. Who wrote *The Waste Land*?

"Bully's bellowed you out there!"

6. What nickname is given to Birdwatchers?

7. What was Ross and Monica's surname in *Friends*?

8. What is the first sign of the Zodiac?

9. What sides meet in the annual University Boat Race?

10. How many degrees are in a right angle?

11. Who had a hit with *January*?

12. They say a leopard never changes, what?

13. Elsie Tanner was a character in which soap?

14. What song gave St Winifred's School Choir a hit?

15. Near which Welsh town was Anthony Hopkins born?

16. In *Eastenders* what was the name of Robbie Jackson's dog?

17. In what country was Archduke Ferdinand shot?

18. In which country would you find Yucatan?

19. Who was Bob Marley's backing band?

20. The natives of what country may be referred to as Hellenes?

Pot Luck 6

1. What is the currency in Aruba?

2. In what city would you find Gorky Park?

3. What D is a young upper class lady being introduced to society?

4. What is the most expensive property in the traditional version of Monopoly?

5. What word was used to describe the non-traditional lifestyles of marginalized and impoverished artists, writers, journalists, musicians, and actors in major European cities?

6. Orange-Nassau are the ruling house of which country?

7. What is the birthstone for September?

8. How many points on a triangle?

9. What is the second largest city in the USA after New York?

10. Who wrote *Rebecca*?

11. What is 13 times 13?

12. How was Sir Percy Blakeney better known?

13. With which other Basketball side have the LA Lakers shared an arena with since 1999?

14. In what town was Tina Turner born?

15. What is the chemical symbol of Aluminium?

16. Who was the lead singer of Marillion from 1981 to 1988?

17. What could be a Shenandoah or a Balbo?

18. For what is William Willett remembered?

19. Where were the 1980 Olympics held?

20. Which Barrel size comes from the Dutch for Small Cask?

"101 or more with 6 darts for tonight's mystery star prize"

Pot Luck 7

1. What was the currency of Spain before the Euro?

2. How did Leon Trotsky die?

3. When were the last débutantes presented at Court in the UK?

4. Who played Charlie Chaplin in the 1992 biopic?

5. Phagophobia is the fear of what?

6. What number did the amplifier go to in Spinal Tap?

"Let's check that with Bully"

7. *My Favourite Things* is a song from what Musical?

8. Who was Tina Turner's husband from 1962 to 1978?

9. On what day of the week does Pancake Day fall?

10. In which soap would you meet the character Harry Cross?

11. What is a cockney's boat?

12. Which composer appears as a character in the film *Gosford Park*?

13. In what county was Bob Marley born?

14. 'Like a band of gypsies we go down the highway' is a line from which Willie Nelson song?

15. How many are there in a Baker's Dozen?

16. On what day of the year was William Shakespeare born?

17. What phrase would the thieves use to enter their den in *Ali Baba*?

18. What is the study of rocks called?

19. Which MP left Sian Lloyd for one of the Cheeky Girls?

20. Which country does Avril Lavigne hail from?

Pot Luck 8

1. In which month is Epiphany?

2. What Duchess was involved in the famous *Headless Man* divorce case?

3. What animal term is used to describe a cricketer being put out without scoring?

4. Frigophobia is a fear of what?

5. In what year was CNN launched?

6. Whose enemies are Blinky, Pinky, Inky and Clyde?

7. What school did Norman Lamont attend?

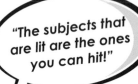

"The subjects that are lit are the ones you can hit!"

8. Which vehicles were used as emergency cover during the Fire Fighters Strike of 2002?

9. What B are the stones used to stabilize a ship?

10. What type of animal is Beatrix Potter's Miss Moppet?

11. Who founded Singapore?

12. Frank Beard is the drummer of which band?

13. What is the second largest city in the Australian state of Victoria?

14. In which park would you find London Zoo?

15. Isaac Hayes won an Oscar for the theme tune to what film?

16. From what language do we get the word balcony?

17. What nationality was Erno Rubik, inventor of the famous cube?

18. In which year did The Gambia achieve independence from Britain?

19. What affluent suburb of Glasgow is the largest town in East Renfrewshire?

20. What is the best possible hand in Poker?

Pot Luck 9

1. Who had a major hit with *D.I.S.C.O*?

2. Which collection of stories do we associate with Sinbad, Aladdin and Ali Baba?

3. Who looked after Orville?

4. What age was William Shakespeare when he died?

5. Who is Yogi Bear's girlfriend?

6. In which English county was Phillip Schofield born?

"Look at what you could have won."

7. What country is the world's largest producer of pepper?

8. What sci-fi drama starred Joanna Lumley and David McCallum?

9. What drink does Fredo ask for in *The Godfather Part 2*?

10. Who wrote *Jane Eyre*?

11. The shows not over until who sings?

12. In what year did Tenzing Norgay die?

13. What is 17% of 200?

14. How many sides does a rectangle have?

15. On which day are Hot Cross Buns usually eaten?

16. What song gave Tina Turner a worldwide smash in 1985?

17. Who officiated at Monica and Chandler's wedding in *Friends*?

18. Where would you find Josie Jump and Archie the Inventor?

19. Who narrates *Come Dine With Me*?

20. What word comes from the capital in Hell in Milton's *Paradise Lost*?

Pot Luck 10

"You've had a good night out - but you go home with nowt!"

1. What is a papoose?

2. What is the shortest month of the year?

3. How many sides does a trapezium have?

4. What Elvis song begins 'Well since my baby left me, I've found a new place to dwell'?

5. What pop magazine closed in 2006?

6. In traditional Monopoly, what square is farthest from the Go square?

7. What collective name was given to Emilio Estevez, Anthony Michael Hall, Rob Lowe, Andrew McCarthy, Demi Moore, Judd Nelson, Molly Ringwald, and Ally Sheedy?

8. Who coined the phrase 'Banana Republic'?

9. What planet was discovered in 1930?

10. What is the second book of the *Bible*?

11. Who wrote the *Young Bond* series of spy novels for teens?

12. Who is Yogi Bear's companion?

13. What arena is home to the LA Lakers?

14. What series number of *Celebrity Juice* began in March 2016?

15. Who murdered Abel?

16. Who won the first series of *Dancing on Ice*?

17. What did Marilyn Monroe wear in bed?

18. What name is given to the group of Senior Politicians who advise the Monarch?

19. Who was the only 'Python' not born in Britain?

20. What colour is a sapphire?

Pot Luck 11

1. What is the highest hill in England?

2. What song contains the line 'rise up this morning, smiled with the rising sun'?

3. How was Saint Petersburg known from 1914 to 1924?

4. Which famous singer was born Anna Mae Bullock?

5. The first of which restaurant chain was opened on 14th June 1971 in Piccadilly, London?

6. What is the name of the Pub in *Eastenders*?

7. What became Sharon's surname after she married Dennis?

8. What type of tea is named after a British Prime Minister?

9. How many gallons in a Kilderkin?

"Throwers and Knowers"

10. The highest point in the Balkans can be found in which country?

11. What American weekly news magazine published in New York City was founded in 1923?

12. Who did Ralf Little play in *The Royle Family*?

13. Bharat is an ancient or romantic name for what country?

14. What river runs through St. Petersburg?

15. What name is given to the form of government where power effectively rests with a small number of people?

16. Who was Orville's arch-enemy?

17. Which children's character lives on the fictional island of Struay?

18. What name is given to the wider and thicker part of a ring?

19. What is the symbol for the chemical element Neodymium?

20. Lytham St Annes lies just to the south of what seaside resort?

Pot Luck 12

1. In which country would you find Ben Gurion Airport?

2. What is Roquefort?

3. Which superhero did Eric Smith become?

4. What is hyperopia?

5. What was the name of *Dennis the Menace's* dog?

6. Who was Phillip Schofield's sidekick on CBBC?

7. Which Elvis song contains the line 'and a hungry little boy with a runny nose'?

8. Which one of the world's richest ever men was born in Dunfermline, Fife?

9. What performance art company have played at the Astor Place Theatre, New York since 1991?

10. What is the closest significant settlement to the point where Oxfordshire, Berkshire and Buckinghamshire meet?

11. La Sagrada Familia cathedral in Barcelona was designed by which Catalan architect?

12. What day of the year is St Patrick's Day celebrated?

13. In what month does Henley Regatta take place?

14. The twins from B*Witched had a brother in which other Pop band?

15. Who is Tom Sawyer infatuated with?

16. Who is Kiefer Sutherland's mother?

17. Which troop look after the security of the Pope?

18. In what country was Edward IV born?

19. How was Suriname known before independence?

20. What was the Lion suit made from in *The Wizard of Oz*?

"Look at what you could have won."

Pot Luck 13

1. What sport features in the film *Match Point*?

2. What village near Rochester gave its name to all Youth prisons?

3. Who did Dirk Benedict play in *The A-Team*?

4. Who was Fanny Craddock's slightly bumbling husband?

5. What slave name was given to Kunta Kinte in *Roots*?

6. What language is spoken in Finland?

7. Which of the Goodies is a keen Birdwatcher?

8. What is the birth name of US President Bill Clinton?

9. Who closed the 2000 Olympics?

10. What is 4 squared?

11. What is Yogi Bear's catchphrase?

12. What is England's oldest weekly magazine aimed at women?

13. How many teaspoons in a table spoon?

14. In which country did Bob Marley die?

15. Which Actress has been Brian May's partner for many years?

16. In what state was Davy Crockett born?

17. What is the name of the dog in Punch and Judy shows?

18. What is known as *The Old Lady of Threadneedle Street*?

19. How could you refer to someone from Newcastle?

20. What is the study of insects called?

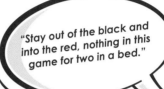

"Stay out of the black and into the red, nothing in this game for two in a bed."

Pot Luck 14

1. Who did Phillip Schofield replace in Joseph and the Amazing Technicolour Dreamcoat?

2. Who wrote Puttin' On the Ritz?

3. What colour is the Reverend in Cluedo?

4. What is the only American state which can be typed using letters from only one row of a QWERTY keyboard?

5. Who is Shakira's partner?

6. Who is Kate Hudson's mother?

7. Who is Jeremy Vine's wisecracking brother?

8. Who is actor Emilio Estevez's brother?

9. Who was married to Antonio Banderas from 1996 to 2014?

10. Who is Melanie Griffith's daughter, star of 50 Shades of Grey?

11. Who is Warren Beatty's elder sister?

12. What is the name of Al Gore's wife?

13. The name of which London area originally meant Landing place for Lambs?

14. What name is often used for an area of Newington near the Strata Tower, it's name arising from a local coaching Inn?

15. In which area of London was David Bowie born?

16. In what area of London can you see The Cutty Sark?

17. In which area of London is the City Hall of the GLA located?

18. What is the only London Tube Station to have 6 consecutive consonants in its name?

19. What London nickname could be given to the young underemployed, often snooty and ostentatiously well-off members of the upper classes?

20. What virus caused panic in Brazil in 2015 and 2016?

"Look at what you could have won."

Pot Luck 15

1. Why was Felix Baumgartner in the news in 2012?

2. Which member of the Bush family dropped out of the 2016 Presidential Race?

3. The revolutions across the Islamic World in 2010 to 2012 were given what name?

4. Whose death kickstarted the 2011 England riots?

5. What police operation was set up to investigate the abuses of Jimmy Saville and others?

6. A serious accident on what ride caused Alton Towers to close in 2015?

7. What does a 'Mars a Day' help you do?

8. What slogan did Wonderbra use successfully in the 90s?

9. What lager was 'reassuringly expensive'?

"And Bully's Special Priiiiize..."

10. In what year was Idi Amin deposed as leader of Uganda?

11. Who ruled Haiti with an iron fist from 1957 to 1971?

12. In what year did Pol Pot die?

13. What political party was Saddam Hussein a member of?

14. Which Dictator once practiced at the Western Eye Hospital, London?

15. In which country was Adolf Hitler born?

16. Who was 'Your Flexible Friend'?

17. 'Don't leave home without it'. Without what?

18. What is the birthstone for March?

19. Who was the manager of The Beatles?

20. What country traditionally goes last in the Olympic opening parade?

Pot Luck 16

1. Which controversial athlete raced at the 1984 Olympics for Britain and the 1992 Olympics for South Africa?

2. In what year were the first Winter Olympics?

"Now the cash you won for charity earlier... that's safe."

3. Who won Gold in the Women's Singles Tennis at London 2012?

4. What nickname was given to the Beijing National Stadium?

5. Where in Britain is 'the Granite City'?

6. The 2 largest slate quarries in the world were once found in which British nation?

7. The largest example of what was found in Moliagul, Victoria, Australia in 1869?

8. Blue John is only found in what county of the UK?

9. Which North Yorkshire town is located near large deposits of the mineral Jet?

10. Which mineral is a parallel banded variety of the oxide mineral chalcedony?

11. Iron pyrite is more commonly known as what?

12. Which Beatles song was written for Mia Farrow's younger sister?

13. Which of the four Beatles was the eldest?

14. Which London street is most associated with the Beatles?

15. Who did Paul McCartney say was the 'Fifth Beatle' in 2016?

16. How many children did Queen Victoria have?

17. How many times was William Gladstone Prime Minister?

18. Who is the only Prime Minister to date to have been born Jewish?

19. Who was Queen Victoria's consort?

20. What was Queen Victoria's first language?

Pot Luck 17

1. At what age did Prince Albert die?

2. Which drink was advertised with the slogan anytime, anyplace, anywhere?

3. What is the advertising slogan of L'Oreal?

4. *Sola scriptura* is the name of the Christian doctrine that says that what is supreme?

5. The Black Pope is the name given to the head of what organisation?

6. What is the holiest city in the religion of Islam?

"Super, smashing, great."

7. What Christian group was formed by Jakob Ammann?

8. What Christian sect thrived in northern Italy and southern France, between the 12th and 14th centuries?

9. What religious text tells of an appearance of Jesus Christ in the Americas shortly after his resurrection?

10. What is the last book of the *Old Testament*?

11. In which religion would you find the Guru Granth Sahib?

12. Which Bible character was said to have been born in Scotland?

13. What name is given to the head of the Catholic Church?

14. What name is given to the Sunday before Easter?

15. Who was the only apostle not martyred?

16. After Spanish Mexicans, which European nationality makes up the next biggest group in Mexico?

17. What is the name of the largest lake in Turkey?

18. What is the longest river in Saudi Arabia?

19. How many square feet in an acre?

20. In which country is the world's steepest street?

Pot Luck 18

1. Yellowstone Lake is located in which US state?

2. What was the most famous song written by Francis Scott Key?

3. In which country did Che Guevara die?

4. What American State is closest to Bermuda?

"Innnnnn six...."

5. In what year did the last remaining Indian King from the days of the British Raj die?

6. Who was the first President of Zimbabwe?

7. What was Capability Brown's occupation?

8. What is the better known name of the Spanish mission San Antonio de Valero?

9. In which country is the tallest dam in the world?

10. Who were the first non-musicians to perform on Band Aid?

11. What Mexican revolutionary nearly started a war with the US when he invaded a town in New Mexico in 1916?

12. What lemon-scented oil is derived from dried grasses and used as an insect repellent?

13. Which country administered the port of Macau until 1999?

14. Who designed the City Hall offices of the Mayor of London?

15. What type of structure could be described as a bascule?

16. Who was the oldest of the Bronte Sisters?

17. According to *The News of the World*, Rebecca Loos conducted an affair with which star?

18. What London street, with many Curry Houses, is known as Banglatown?

19. In what London Borough is Canary Wharf?

20. What is the family name of the Dukes of Devonshire?

Pot Luck 19

1. What is the historic home of the Marquess of Salisbury?

2. Who is the father of Jade Goody's children?

3. How did Director Tony Scott commit suicide?

4. How did King Juan Carlos of Spain's brother die?

5. If you are ill it could be said you were 'under the…' what?

6. Who is the current Prime Minister of India?

7. What is the name of the National Rail operator in Iceland?

8. Ryanair's HQ can be found in what country?

"You win nothing but your BFH… Bus Fare Home"

9. Why might a Chinook leave you shaken?

10. Cheryl started dating which One Direction star in 2015?

11. What did *FHM* stand for in the magazine name?

12. One German won the title of FHM Sexiest Woman in the World. Who was it?

13. Two women have been voted FHM Sexiest Woman in the World twice. Name them.

14. Who designed the Royal Pavilion in Brighton?

15. What name is given to the annual list of the 500 biggest companies in America?

16. In which country would you find the Burj Khalifa and The World Islands?

17. What city is believed to have the most expensive hotel rooms in the world?

18. What Sea separates Southeastern Europe from Western Asia?

19. How often are leap years?

20. What country came into being on the 23rd February 1854?

Prime Ministers

1. In what year was David Cameron born?

2. What was Gordon Brown's father's occupation?

3. Who was Prime Minister at the start of the 20th Century?

4. What was Sir Henry Campbell-Bannerman's seat whilst Prime Minister?

5. How many elections did Margaret Thatcher win?

6. In what city was Tony Blair born?

"101 or more with 6 darts for tonight's mystery star prize"

7. Who was the Prime Minister at the outbreak of WW2?

8. Who was Prime Minister at the end of WW2?

9. As a child, in which country did Tony Blair live for 3 years?

10. Which Prime Minister was nicknamed The Welsh Wizard?

11. How many elections were won by John Major?

12. What political problem led to the end of Anthony Eden's Premiership?

13. In what year did Harold Wilson first become PM?

14. Which PM is buried in Ringmer, East Sussex?

15. Which constituency did Ramsay MacDonald represent when he first became PM?

16. Who was Prime Minister at the time of Princess Diana's death?

17. Which Prime Minister took Britain into the EEC?

18. What is the name of the Prime Minister's country house?

19. Who is sometimes referred to as 'The Unknown Prime Minister'?

20. What was the name of Tony Blair's student band?

Real Names

1. Which wrestler had the real name Roderick Toombs?

2. Which World famous singer was born Katy Hudson?

3. What is Joaquin Phoenix's real surname?

4. Which famous actor was born Krishna Pandit Bhanji?

5. Which MASH star was born Alphonso Joseph D'Abruzzo?

6. What is Tiger Woods' real first name?

7. How is Agnes Gonxha Bojaxhiu better known?

8. What was Paul Daniels' real first name?

9. What was Capability Brown's real first name?

10. How was Terence 'Terry' Nelhams-Wright better known?

11. Whose real name was Doris Mary Ann Kappelhoff?

12. What is Rihanna's real first name?

13. What is Actor David Tennant's real name?

14. Whose real name was Shirley Crabtree?

15. How was actress Natalia Zacharenko better known?

16. Which star was born Lee Jun-fan?

17. Who was born Nicholas Kim Coppola?

18. Eric Blair was the real name of which author?

19. How is singer Derek Dick better known?

20. Whose real name is Anthony Paul Beke?

"All for the throw of a dart"

Reality TV

1. Who did Sam Fox swap with on *Celebrity Wife Swap*?

2. Which British-Nigerian won the 8th series of *Big Brother*?

3. Which star of *TOWIE* died in December 2015?

4. In what year did *TOWIE* begin?

"Go for your lights"

5. Which former *Big Brother* contestant claims to have thought up the idea for *TOWIE*, and indeed received a settlement from ITV?

6. Who is the oldest Kardashian?

7. Which reality TV star started on *TOWIE* but has since went on to star in *Splash*, *I'm a Celebrity Get me out of here* and *The Jump*?

8. Andy Cohen is the Executive Producer of what set of reality programmes?

9. Which reality TV show launched the career of Ben Fogle?

10. Which *Big Brother* star caused a race row with Shilpa Shetty?

11. Which has been the biggest-selling UK *X Factor* winner's single to date?

12. In which reality TV series are holidaymakers shook up when their former boyfriends and girlfriends join them?

13. Scotty T has appeared on numerous Reality TV shows, what does the T stand for?

14. Who supposedly pleasured a pig in the first series of The Farm?

15. On which show did Luisa Zissman make her name?

16. In which series of the mid 2000s were Chavs taught how to be traditional 'ladies'?

17. What was controversial about the show *I Wanna Marry Harry*?

18. Who has hosted 15 series of *American Idol*?

19. Who won the British version of *Hit Me Baby One More Time*?

20. Which reality TV show of 2005 had such poor ratings that it was axed after just 5 shows?

Religion 1

1. Which Mormon leader led his people through the desert to Utah?

2. What would a Creationist not believe in?

3. What is the symbol of the Freemasons?

4. What is the usual age for a Jewish boy to celebrate his Bar Mitzvah?

5. What is the number of the Beast?

6. What is the special word used to describe a Church used as a destination for a pilgrimage?

7. If Adam was the first man, who was the first woman?

8. Science and Health is a key text in which religion?

9. Who was the leader of the Branch Davidians at the time of the Waco Siege?

10. Which large Christian denomination observes Saturday as the Sabbath?

11. Who is the leader of the Roman Catholic church?

12. What is usually placed as the last book of the Bible?

13. What was the occupation of Joseph, husband of Mary?

14. Who is traditionally considered the first apostle to be martyred?

15. How many theses did Martin Luther pin to the door?

16. What is the name of the Pope's Ring?

17. Who was the first General of the Salvation Army?

18. In which city did John Knox meet John Calvin?

19. Who is the Indian Goddess of Destruction?

20. Which Brothers were leaders in the foundation of the Methodist Church?

"You've got the time it takes for the board to revolve..."

Religion 2

1. In the coat of arms of the Pope, what colour are the Crossed Keys?

2. Who became the first Pope to resign since 1451?

3. What year did Padre Pio die?

4. What name is given in the Christian faith to describe body marks, sores, or sensations of pain in locations corresponding to the crucifixion wounds of Jesus Christ?

5. What percentage of people in Utah are Mormons?

6. How are members of the Religious Society of Friends known?

7. Who was the first person to see Jesus when he rose from the dead?

8. Who is credited with bringing Christianity to Scotland?

9. What date is St. Swithin's Day?

10. Who is the patron saint of Glasgow?

11. Which Saint has his shrine in Durham Cathedral?

12. Who was the first recorded British martyr?

13. An ampoule of whose blood is displayed at Naples cathedral 3 times a year?

14. Who is the patron saint of animals?

15. Which Saint was the mother of the Emperor Constantine the Great, and thereby a key person in the introduction of Christianity to the West?

16. Which Saint was murdered at Canterbury Cathedral in 1170?

17. Who is the Patron Saint of London?

18. Ravenglass in Cumbria claims to be the birthplace of what Saint?

19. What is the symbol of St Mark?

20. Who was the first drunk mentioned in the Bible?

"Remember, you can't beat a bit of Bully!"

Science

1. Can dogs breed with wolves?

2. DDT is an organic chemical, what does DDT stand for?

3. On the periodic table, an element's atomic number represents the number of what in its atom?

4. What is the chemical symbol for table salt?

5. Who created the first published Periodic Table of Elements?

6. Which element is named after a Scottish village?

7. Which country is named after the element silver?

8. Organic Chemistry always involves what element?

9. What is the first element of the Periodic Table?

10. An atom will usually consist of Protons, Electrons and what else?

11. What is the opposite of an acid?

12. Which woman won the Nobel Prize for Chemistry in 1911?

13. What colour is coal?

14. Which gas makes up the biggest portion of the air we breathe?

15. Which element has the symbol Sn?

16. What granular substance is the main ingredient of glass?

17. What chemical is being searched for in *Avatar*?

18. What group term is often used to describe the 15 lanthanides, Scandium and Yttrium?

19. Which country is the world's biggest producers of potassium?

20. What is Robert Bunsen's most famous invention?

"Bully's bellowed you out there!"

Soaps

1. Which *Brookside* character was played by Dean Sullivan?

2. Who played Nasty Nick Cotton in *Eastenders*?

3. In which London Square is *Eastenders* set?

4. How many times did Coronation Street's Deirdre Barlow marry?

5. Who did Todd Carty play in *Eastenders* from 1990 to 2003?

6. Helen Worth has been in more episodes than anyone else of which soap?

7. Who played Dot Cotton in *Eastenders* for many years?

8. Which soap gave us JR, Sue Ellen and Cliff?

9. Who is Alfie Moon's younger brother in *Eastenders*?

10. When did Barbara Windsor join *Eastenders*?

11. Who did Larry Hagman play in *Dallas*?

12. Who did Wendy Richards play in *Eastenders* for many years?

13. Which soap would you associate with Harold Bishop?

14. Who plays Whitney Dean in *Eastenders*?

15. *The Colbys* was a spin-off from which other soap?

16. Who played Peter Barlow for many years in *Coronation Street*?

17. What soap achieved the highest ratings on Channel 5's launch night?

18. In what street is *Neighbours* set?

19. What is the name of the pub in *Coronation Street*?

20. What is Kevin Webster's job in *Coronation Street*?

"101 or more with 6 darts for tonight's mystery star prize"

Sport and Games 1

1. Where did Wimbledon FC play their home games until 1991?

2. Which future England Captain helped Ipswich win the UEFA Cup in 1981?

3. Who scored with both his head and feet for England at the 1990 World Cup?

4. Which North Eastern team are best remembered for their 1978 cup run?

5. Which team plays at Old Trafford?

"Let's check that with Bully"

6. What was unusual about Mo Johnston's signing for Rangers in 1989?

7. Where did Leicester City play their home games until 2002?

8. Maradona scored 'The Hand of God' against England, in what stadium?

9. Which country's national side play at the largest football ground (by seating capacity) in the world?

10. For which Italian side did David Platt sign in 1991?

11. What evasive football move is named after a Dutch footballer?

12. Who set a British Goalkeeping record by playing 1196 consecutive minutes of competitive football without conceding a goal?

13. Who captained England against Holland in March 2016?

14. Where do Hibs play?

15. Who is the only footballer to have won the World Player of the Year 5 times?

16. How many squares on a chess board?

17. Which colour usually starts first in a game of Chess?

18. Who succeeded Bobby Fischer as World Chess Champion?

19. What is the acronym for the World Chess organising body?

20. Which British Nigel challenged for the Chess World Championship in the 1990s?

Sport and Games 2

1. How many different characters are there in the game *Guess Who*?

2. Which chess piece can only move diagonally?

3. In which game do you attempt to solve the murder of Mr. Black?

4. In which game would you use the term checkmate?

5. In which game would you get a double top?

6. In what game do you collect wedges before moving to the centre?

7. At what game was Omar Sharif once ranked one of the best players in the world?

8. How many squares may a pawn move on its first go?

9. At the end of 2015 who was World Chess Champion?

10. What is considered the first modern role playing game?

11. What do Americans call Noughts and Crosses?

12. The phrase 'Back to Square One' possibly has its route in the playing of what children's board game?

13. In which game do you have to carefully place items on a mule's back?

14. In which game would you collect Blue and Pink 'People Pegs'?

15. How many cards are you dealt in a game of 'Texas Hold'em' poker?

16. How many people play in a game of Mah Jong?

17. In charades, what word is indicated by making a T sign with your fingers?

18. In what decade did crosswords first appear?

19. In what drinking game must you drink if you have done what the questioner hasn't?

20. In what game is the aim to occupy all the territories on Earth?

"The subjects that are lit are the ones you can hit!"

Sport and Games 3

1. 'A3', 'Miss'. In what game might you hear this exchange?

2. The creators of Trivial Pursuit set out to make their own game after they found missing pieces in what they intended to play. What game was it they intended to play?

3. What do you draw from the tube in Ker Plunk?

4. Which 2 British World Champion Boxers met for a Super Bantamweight showdown in February 2016?

5. What sport was Max Baer a top exponent of?

6. Which horse won the Grand National 3 times in the 1970s?

7. At which track is the King George VI Chase usually ran?

"All for the throw of a dart"

8. Which ex-jockey went on to write over 40 international best-selling books?

9. What was the nickname of Martin Offiah?

10. In Snooker, what is the blue ball worth?

11. Generally speaking, what colour is the felt on a Snooker table?

12. Who took 708 test wickets for Australia?

13. In Motor Racing, who has been described as "the greatest driver never to win the World Championship"?

14. Which Frenchman claims to be the founder of freerunning?

15. Who are the local rivals of Kaizer Chiefs F.C.?

16. What name was given to the 3 all-conquering golfers of the first years of the 20th Century?

17. The PDC is a governing organisation in what sport?

18. How wide are the goals in football?

19. With whom did Jamie Murray win the 2007 Mixed Doubles at Wimbledon?

20. What sport was played professionally by Ronan Rafferty?

Sport and Games 4

1. What is the name of the line you stand behind in darts?

2. What is the name of the object struck in a game of Badminton?

3. What is the name of the object struck in a game of Ice Hockey?

4. Which football team is based in South Norwood, London?

5. How many players are there in a rugby team?

6. What is the highest possible check-out in Darts?

7. Which country won the most Gold Medals at the 2012 Olympics?

8. Which former rugby player once called the English RFU committee 'Old Farts'?

9. What sport is played at The WACA?

10. In Cricket, what name is given to a specialist Batsman who comes in to bat before the close of play?

11. In English Cricket, when were the rules changed to make it a 6-Ball over?

12. Frankie Fredericks ran for which country?

13. For which American Football team did OJ Simpson play for the bulk of his career?

14. Which German football club won the league 5 times in the 1970s?

15. Who defeated Wladimir Klitschko to become the unified World Heavyweight Boxing World Champion in 2015?

16. Where was the 2014 Ryder Cup held?

17. Which Brit won the Ladies 400m Hurdles title in 2014?

18. Who is the youngest person to have been capped for the England football team?

19. Who is the oldest person to have been capped by the England football team?

20. In Cricket, which English bowler has taken more wickets than any other?

"You've had a good night out - but you go home with nowt!"

Sport and Games 5

1. Who was the first person to defeat Muhammad Ali?

2. In golf, what name is given to the pre-determined number of strokes to complete a hole?

3. In which sport is the Stanley Cup competed for?

4. Where were the Olympic Games held in 1984?

5. At what age did Rafael Nadal turn professional?

6. How many points for the Brown ball in Snooker?

7. What is Venus Williams' middle name?

8. Who was defeated in the World Championship Snooker final six times?

9. Joss Naylor is considered the best competitor in his sport. What sport was it?

10. Who was the surprise winner of the 1986 Snooker World Championships?

11. Which British female tennis player reached the Semi Finals of the 2016 Australian Open?

12. Which cricketer shares the record for playing the most seasons of first class cricket?

13. In which game do you throw hollow metal balls at the jack whilst keeping both feet on the ground?

14. In Wrestling, who was Big Daddy's Arch Enemy?

15. In what sport would you find a Spider and a Triangle?

16. What age was Virginia Wade when she won Wimbledon?

17. Leighton Aspell is a famous name in which sport?

18. Who was the first Darts World Champion?

19. In what outdoor activity do people use GPS locators to find containers?

20. Brett Favre is most associated with which NFL team?

"Throwers and Knowers"

Sport and Games 6

1. What sport is Dan Purvis an Olympic medal winner?

2. In which sport is Earl The Pearl Strickland a well known name?

3. In which decade was Muhammad Ali born?

4. Which running distance is sometimes described as 'the metric mile'?

5. Which Brit won Silver on the Pommel Horse at the 2012 Olympic Games?

6. Who managed England at the 2003 Rugby World Cup?

7. What England Rugby star of the 90s was 'Prince of Centres'?

8. How many Olympic Gold medals has Tom Daley won?

"Super, smashing, great."

9. In what sport was Doug Mountjoy a top player?

10. What sport takes place on bikes which only have one gear and no brakes?

11. What stadium hosts the English Greyhound Derby?

12. Which country with a population of 157 million people has never won an Olympic medal?

13. Who coached the Scottish Rugby side to their 1990 Grand Slam victory?

14. Nick Easter has represented England at which sport?

15. What sport was invented by Walter Clopton Wingfield?

16. Who is the current sponsor of The Grand National?

17. Who was Helen Rollason?

18. The Chicago Blackhawks compete in which sport?

19. What is the name of the computer which spots wayward shots at Wimbledon?

20. Who was WBC Heavyweight Champion at the end of 1995?

Sport and Games 7

1. Which American Heavyweight famously retired undefeated in 1956?

2. What Sport is sometimes referred to as Gridiron?

3. What Cricketer was known as 'Beefy'?

4. Which cricket side play in Chester Le Street?

5. Which Darts player has won the World Championship 16 times?

6. How many points for a win in English football?

7. Which Englishman managed Barcelona from 1984 to 1987?

8. Which female American sprinter won 3 Gold medals at the Seoul Olympics?

9. At what age did Tiger Woods turn professional?

10. Who are the most successful football team in the world

11. The Borg-Warner Trophy is awarded to the winner of which race?

12. How many players in a Beach Volleyball team?

13. Which sport is played on the largest pitch?

14. In what kind of football do players move around the floor on their hands and feet?

15. Which female British swimmer won 2 gold medals at the 2008 Olympics?

16. For which club side did Rugby star Martin Johnson play?

17. What is the first horse racing classic of the calendar year?

18. Who invented basketball?

19. Which boxer was known as Stonefist?

20. Which Edinburgh Boxer is regarded as the greatest British lightweight boxer in history?

"Stay out of the black and into the red, nothing in this game for two in a bed."

Sport and Games 8

1. Which boxer's nickname was 'Second to'?

2. Which England cricketer was killed in a car crash in 2002?

3. Where were the Commonwealth Games held in 2002?

4. Who was the losing finalist in the 1995 Snooker World Championship?

5. What game is played on a Diamond?

6. With what sport would you associate Edward Payson Weston?

7. Who captained the British Lions on their 1989 tour of Australia?

8. Who won the Male singles in the year that Virginia Wade won the Women's Singles?

9. Who was the first woman from a Scandinavian country to hold the World Number one spot in tennis?

10. On 30th May 2015, who became the leading run-scorer in Test matches for England?

11. Who was the tennis player Martina Hingis named after?

12. Fairyhouse is best known as a venue for which sport?

13. Which Brit won the IndyCar Series in 2007, 2009, 2010 and 2011?

14. Which Scot drove in Formula One from 2010 to 2013?

15. What is the highest score available with 3 throws in Darts?

16. What is the name of the Seattle NFL team?

17. Which sport do the Vancouver Whitecaps play?

18. How often is the Ryder Cup held?

19. What is the most Northerly League Football ground in the UK?

20. Where was the Ryder Cup held in 2014?

"Now the cash you won for charity earlier... that's safe."

The Arts

1. Who painted the *Mona Lisa*?

2. The National Gallery stands in which London Square?

3. What is regarded as Edvard Munch's most famous work?

4. The Salvador Dali painting *The Persistence of Memory* features what item melting?

5. The film *Lust for Life* was about what artist's life?

6. What was the first name of *Constable*?

"Super, smashing, great."

7. For what subject was painter George Stubbs famed?

8. What did Christy Brown use to paint?

9. What painting was stolen in broad daylight from a museum in Oslo in 2004?

10. Who was a man not forestalled by predecessors, nor to be classed with contemporaries, nor to be replaced by known or readily surmisable successors'?

11. Pablo Picasso pioneered which area of Art, considered the most influential art movement of the 20th century?

12. Who painted *The House with the Cracked Walls*?

13. Who sculpted the *Ecstasy of Saint Teresa*?

14. Which Chinese artist filled the Tate with sunflower seeds?

15. Who sculpted the statue of Jan Smuts in Parliament Square, London?

16. Who was the best-known practitioner of the literary school of naturalism?

17. With which Art movement do we associate Andy Warhol?

18. Which artist is most famous for his paintings of *Matchstick Men*?

19. Who painted *The Nightwatch*?

20. What is Johannes Vermeer most famous painting?

The Final Frontier

1. Who did Sigourney Weaver play in the *Alien* Franchise?

2. What Oscar Winner turned down the role of Spock in *Star Trek*?

3. Which 2012 Science Fiction movie was inspired by a board game?

4. What was the tagline of *Alien*?

5. What was H.G. Wells' first novel?

6. Who was the 3rd *Dr Who*?

7. What was Mr Spock's blood group?

8. How many moons does the planet Neptune have?

9. What scientific theory puts forward that after an initial expansion, the universe cooled sufficiently to allow the formation of subatomic particles, and later simple atoms?

10. What was the name of the spacecraft that landed on the moon with Neil Armstrong?

11. Which planet is famous for its rings?

12. What is known as the Red Planet?

13. Which planet is famous for its big red spot?

14. What name do we give the belts of radiation that circle the earth?

15. How often do full moons occur?

16. How often does Halley's comet appear?

17. What comet was dubbed 'the great comet of 1997'?

18. Which University did Tim Peake attend?

19. What series name was given to the first Space Shuttles?

20. What name is given to Chinese Astronauts?

"Innnnnn seven..."

The Human Body

1. How would we usually describe a solid blister on our hands?

2. What is the longest bone in the human body?

3. Where would you find your metatarsal?

4. What is someone with alopecia losing?

5. What part of her body is Heather Mills missing?

6. What viral disease is also known as herpes zoster?

"You win nothing but your BFH... Bus Fare Home"

7. What is lactation?

8. What do Americans call acid reflux?

9. What disease is an inflammatory response in the lungs resulting in narrowing of the small airways and breakdown of lung tissue?

10. What name is given to the study of diseases involving the respiratory tract?

11. What part of your body will a podiatrist look after?

12. What parts of your body does a neurosurgeon look after?

13. What great artery leads out from the left of the heart?

14. Which part of the body would you find rods and cones?

15. Which element is fundamental for healthy teeth and bones?

16. Where in your body will you find the anvil?

17. Which organ of the body produces insulin?

18. A sphygmomanometer measures what in the human body?

19. Where might plantar issues hurt you?

20. What P is your smallest finger?

The Royal Family

1. At what University did Prince William and Kate Middleton meet?

2. Who is Kate Middleton's sister?

3. What Stone, used in the coronation of Scottish Kings, is fitted below the Coronation Thrones?

4. Who is older, Prince William or Prince Harry?

5. Who were Prince William's first 2 children?

6. Which royal married Antony Armstrong-Jones?

7. At what age did Edward VII ascend to the throne?

8. Does the Queen have a driving licence?

"101 or more with 6 darts for tonight's mystery star prize"

9. Who had the shortest reign of the 20th century?

10. What was the name of the Queen Mother's brother who died in WWI?

11. Which actress did Lord Frederick Windsor marry?

12. Which of the Queen's cousins is the Grand Master of the Grand Lodge of Mark Master Masons?

13. Who is the Queen's oldest grandchild?

14. Who was Prince Philip's best man?

15. Where did Charles and Diana marry?

16. Where did Charles and Camilla marry?

17. What is the Queen's official residence in Northern Ireland?

18. In what year was Prince Edward born?

19. In what country did the former Edward VIII pass away?

20. What was the family home of Lady Diana Spencer before her marriage to Prince Charles?

The World 1

1. Who has the biggest ears, African Elephants or Indian Elephants?

2. What is the smallest mammal in the UK?

3. What is the meat of an older sheep called?

4. What name is often given to the feral free roaming horses of the American Plains?

5. Which aquatic egg laying mammals are native to Eastern Australia and Tasmania?

6. What kind of animal is a Silverback?

7. What is the most popular dog breed in the US?

8. What is a female donkey called?

"All for the throw of a dart"

9. Which big cat can run faster than any other land animal?

10. What city was the capital of Australia from 1901 to 1927?

11. What is the capital of Greenland?

12. What city is the capital of Italy?

13. What is the capital of Iceland?

14. What country is bigger in size, Ukraine or Belarus?

15. True or False - Norway has a border with Russia?

16. How many stars appear on the Australian flag?

17. What colours make up the Union Jack?

18. What tree appears on the flag of Lebanon?

19. What are the 2 main colours of the flag of Spain?

20. What colour is the cross on the flag of Finland?

The World 2

1. What is the main colour of the flag of Switzerland?

2. What colours made up the flag of the German Empire from 1866 to 1918?

3. What colour was the flag of Libya?

4. What is the colour of the flag of al-Qaeda?

5. How many stars are on the Chinese flag?

"Go for your lights"

6. What is the name of the official residence of the French President?

7. What is the capital city of the French region of Languedoc?

8. The inhabitants of which French town are known as Aixois?

9. What word comes from the French for a seller of medicines who might advertise his presence with music and an outdoor stage show?

10. In which French resort would you find the luxurious Hôtel du Palais?

11. What name was given to French Protestants?

12. Who led the French at Waterloo?

13. What word is used to describe the eldest son of the King of France?

14. What is the third colour on the French Flag after Red and White?

15. Which Frenchman founded the International Olympic Committee?

16. Which Baron carried out massive works in the city of Paris?

17. How many avenues meet at the Arc De Triomphe in Paris?

18. In what tunnel did Princess Diana die?

19. What was President Mitterrand's first name?

20. In what year did Ireland first issue its own stamps as an independent country?

The World 3

1. Who was the first President of Ireland?

2. What is the name of the official residence of the Irish President?

3. Where is *The Book of Kells* on display?

4. What is the most Southwesterly province of Ireland?

5. Where would you find Karol Wojtyła Airport?

6. Which Italian city, the capital of Tuscany, is famous for the Duomo?

7. In which city do Internazionale play?

8. Which volcano dominates the skyline of Naples?

9. What is the largest island in Italy?

10. Where would you find the Yazoo River?

11. What is the longest river in England?

12. In which country is the mouth of the Mekong River?

13. Which River traditionally forms the border between Scotland and England?

14. The Great Pee Dee River flows into what body of water?

15. On which river does Hull lie?

16. What river runs through Rome?

17. In which country will you find the River Po?

18. At the mouth of which river will you find The Nore?

19. What river runs through Prague?

20. Which river flows into the Dead Sea?

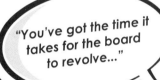

"You've got the time it takes for the board to revolve..."

The World 4

1. The Volga river is the main river that flows into which inland sea?

2. What is the longest river in France?

3. Which river flows through Budapest?

4. On which river does Baghdad stand?

5. What River runs through Washington DC?

6. What is Canada's largest city?

7. What is Canada's biggest export?

8. What is the largest territory of Canada?

9. The Canadian city of Windsor is linked to what US City?

10. What city is home to the Oriental Pearl Tower?

11. How is Santa referred to in Brazil, Uruguay and Argentina?

12. Which country is named after an Italian city?

13. What is the smallest country in the world?

14. Where are The Dardanelles?

15. In which country would you find the Maasai Mara National Reserve?

16. What is the currency of Iceland?

17. What was a Deutschmark split up into?

18. Who was the first chancellor of the reunited Germany?

19. What city is the capital of Bavaria?

20. Who is credited with securing India for the British Crown?

"All for the throw of a dart"

The World 5

1. Who was the first Prime Minister of India?

2. What Indian criminals would gain the confidence of travellers before strangling them with a cloth?

3. Which Hindu God is usually described as having the dark complexion of water-filled clouds and having four arms?

4. On what specific island is Pearl Harbour located?

5. What island is known as The Emerald Isle of the Caribbean?

6. Which town is considered the capital of the Isle of Wight?

7. What small island lies off the Southern point of the Isle of Man?

8. What island was the scene of a nuclear accident in 1979?

9. What is the largest of the Channel Islands?

10. What is the largest of the Dodecanese Islands?

11. Thule Air Base, the United States Air Force's most northernmost base, is on which island?

12. What symbol appears on the flag of Israel?

13. Who is the only female Prime Minister of Israel?

14. What is the name of the National Intelligence Agency of Israel?

15. In which country was Shimon Peres born?

16. What is the most important and ancient cemetery in Jerusalem?

17. Which Israeli prime minister was assassinated in 1995?

18. In what year did Israel declare independence?

19. Who was the Roman god of fire?

20. Who was the first emperor of Rome?

"You can't beat a bit of Bully!"

The World 6

1. In the Roman world what was Garum?

2. Which General attacked Rome after leading his army, including Elephants, over The Alps?

3. What was the name of the 73 miles constructed by the Romans across modern day Northern England?

4. Which Roman General is regarded as the father of Guerilla Warfare?

5. Who were the main opposing forces in the Punic Wars?

6. What is the most common pub name in the UK?

7. What is the second highest mountain in the UK?

"Remember, you can't beat a bit of Bully!"

8. Which city suffered a devastating Helicopter crash in 2013?

9. What could be described as a rapidly rotating storm system characterized by a low-pressure centre, strong winds and a spiral arrangement of gusts that produce heavy rain?

10. Which weather trend is associated with a band of warm ocean water that develops in the central and east-central equatorial Pacific?

11. What heavy industrial company is most associated with Shipbuilding in Belfast?

12. Where can the longest Narrow Gauge Steam train line in Britain be found?

13. On which island will you find *Fingal's Cave*?

14. Kilroot, an ancient salt mine, is located in which area of the UK?

15. How many cents in a quarter?

16. What is the largest city in the state of Wisconsin?

17. The name of which prominent Apache means 'The One Who Yawns'?

18. When completed, the world's largest equine sculpture will be in honour of which Native American leader?

19. Sitting Bull and Crazy Horse were members of which branch of the Sioux?

20. The language of which Native American tribe was used to pass messages by the US Army in WW2 as it was not understood by the Japanese?

Toys

1. What popular toy could be described as a rubber ball with handles?

2. Which toy caused a stampede in the shops at Christmas 1996?

3. Theodore Roosevelt is remembered in the name of which ever popular childhood toy?

4. What handheld video game device was brought out by Nintendo in 1989?

5. Who is Barbie's boyfriend?

6. Which flat grey screened toy was released in 1960?

"Bully's bellowed you out there!"

7. Which Plush Teddy Bears starred in three 80's films?

8. What is the only traditional Monopoly Street on the south side of the River Thames?

9. *Take Me To The River* is a song associated with which Fishy toy popular in the early 2000s?

10. Which children's toy consists of two discs and a string?

11. Which London store is the oldest Toy Shop in the world?

12. Which toy company is known for producing foam based weaponry?

13. Who is the victim in UK Cluedo?

14. In which shape shifting game do all the pieces comprise of four blocks?

15. In what game do you take turns removing wooden blocks from a tower?

16. Which toy was names the world's biggest brand in 2015?

17. Which controversial transport toy was banned in the UK before Christmas 2015?

18. Which inventor launched Dinky cars?

19. What was the Toy of the Year in 1993?

20. Which children's toy has its roots in tilting training tools for jousting practice?

Transport 1

"101 or more with 6 darts for tonight's mystery star prize"

1. Which motorway runs between Glasgow and Edinburgh?

2. What was the name of the famous half-cab London buses?

3. Which entrepreneur is a major backer of Hyperloop train development?

4. Who is the controversial CEO of Ryanair?

5. What does 'vespa' mean in Italian?

6. Igor Sikorsky is associated with the development of which form of transport?

7. Which Toyota model went through the 40m sales mark in the 2000s?

8. Raleigh are most known for producing which form of transport?

9. Who is most remembered for designing the Mini?

10. 'The Clockwork Orange' is an apt nickname for which city's subway system?

11. Which airport is reckoned to be the busiest international airport in the world?

12. Which British airport has a plaque commemorating Elvis Presley?

13. In what year was the Automobile Association formed?

14. What nickname was given to the 1865 Locomotives Act due to its draconian measures?

15. In which year did the Hindenburg explode?

16. Which company owned the Titanic?

17. Which father of modern transport was born in Wylam, Northumberland?

18. The name of which form of transport means 'Smooth Transition'?

19. What was the first US city to have a subway system?

20. What brand of motorcycle does Tom Cruise ride in the 1986 movie *Top Gear*?

Transport 2

1. In what year did the construction of the A1 begin?

2. What is the name of the famous staircase lock on the Caledonian Canal?

3. Which Guildford company are best known for the production of fire engines?

4. What form of transport could be described as a small human-powered watercraft propelled by the action of pedals turning a paddle wheel?

5. What shape are Give Way signs?

6. Bill Lear is most associated with which form of transport?

7. What is the 3-Letter code for O'Hare Airport?

8. How is Idlewild Airport now known?

"Let's check that with Bully"

9. If you landed at CDG airport, which city is it likely you will be visiting?

10. The Mersey Ferry runs from Liverpool to where?

11. What airport is London's second-largest international airport and the second-busiest (by total passenger traffic) in the United Kingdom?

12. What 284 miles long road runs from London to Land's End?

13. What canal links the Atlantic and the Pacific oceans?

14. What nickname is usually given to the ultra fast Shinkansen train?

15. What side of the road do we drive on in the UK?

16. What side of the road do they drive on in Australia?

17. What is the longest motorway in the UK?

18. What motorway runs from Glasgow to Gretna?

19. In which Italian city is the motor manufacturer Fiat based?

20. Which car manufacturer is based in Martorell near Barcelona?

Trivia Time 1

1. What was the follow-up book to *Bridget Jones's Diary*?

2. How did Scarlett and Rhett's daughter die in *Gone with the Wind*?

3. What country is Zanzibar a part of?

4. Adolfo Nicolás is the head of what religious order?

5. What is the primary sacred language of Hinduism?

6. What is the Christian name of Inspector Maigret?

7. What does a barometer do?

8. What name did Anton LaVey give to his youngest child?

9. As of March 2016 who is the King of Spain?

10. What political post is currently held by Mark Harper?

11. What word is used to describe a type of song, usually religious, specifically written for the purpose of adoration or prayer?

12. Where will you find the northernmost trolleybus system on earth?

13. Which American was nicknamed 'The Father of Satanism'?

14. What battle is being depicted in the painting *The Thin Red Line*?

15. Who wrote the novel *The Hundred and One Dalmatians*?

16. On what London street will you find the British Library?

17. Who is the only player to complete more than 30,000 runs in international cricket?

18. What is the primary outflow of the Adriatic?

19. Who wrote *Gone With the Wind*?

20. What is the largest living bird on earth?

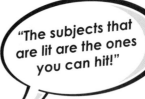

"The subjects that are lit are the ones you can hit!"

Trivia Time 2

1. Which Scouser played for Osasuna in the late 80s?

2. In *Transformers*, who is the leader of the Autobots?

3. What date of the year is Boxing Day?

4. In what year was the UK Driving test introduced?

5. Who sang *Baggy Trousers*?

6. Where was the Mau Mau Uprising?

7. Which song begins 'This Romeo is bleeding, but you can't see his blood'?

8. The Mohawk Valley formula is a plan for breaking what?

9. What was America's most visited city in 2009?

10. What name is given to a large gathering of Scouts?

11. How high are the goals in football?

12. Who became the first overseas-born player to represent Yorkshire?

13. What is the more common name for the bone called the furcula, found in birds?

14. What charity was set up by people in showbusiness to help disadvantaged children?

15. What was the title of the Emperor of Russia?

16. What kind of a car was *Herbie*?

17. What is the largest city in Manitoba?

18. Who composed *La Boheme*?

19. What country has the second largest population?

20. What is the highest mountain in Wales?

"Up to the oche - and listen to Tony!"

Trivia Time 3

1. What nation is named for the Hapsburg king of Spain from 1556 to 1598?

2. What name is given to a religious celebration that can be moved to different dates on different years?

3. In what year did Kenya win independence?

4. What was the name of King Arthur's sword?

5. How many sides are there on a 50p coin?

6. Who was Member of Parliament for Plymouth Sutton from 1974 to 1992?

7. Which Conservative MP was at the centre of the 2012 'Plebgate' scandal?

8. A country's wealth is sometimes talked about as its GDP. What does GDP stand for?

9. What is London Particular?

10. Who played Screech in *Saved By The Bell*?

11. In what year was Rasputin killed?

12. Where does the Welsh Grand National take place?

13. What is Dr. Watson's first name in the *Sherlock Holmes* stories?

14. Complete the saying, 'as safe as…'?

15. What treaty led to the creation of a borderless area within the European Union?

16. What is the bestselling newspaper in the UK?

17. What company produce Digestive biscuits?

18. Who was captured on the 13th December 2003?

19. How many cards in a Tarot Deck?

20. Which war of the 1750s and 60s is sometimes regarded as the first true World War?

"You've had a good night out - but you go home with nowt!"

Trivia Time 4

1. Who sang *Robert De Niro's Waiting*?

2. In what year did Leonard Bernstein die?

3. What is the term for an architectural structure sited to take advantage of a fine or scenic view?

4. The Khmer Rouge was a name for the Communist regime which ruled which country between 1975 and 1979?

5. What is the name of the father in Family Guy?

6. What company is the Suez Canal's biggest customer?

"Throwers and Knowers"

7. What is the official religion of Cambodia?

8. What name is given to the structures that prevent sand from moving along a beach?

9. What is St. Elmo's fire?

10. In what year did Poland join the European Union?

11. What Muslim sect from Lebanon do not follow the 'Five Pillars of Islam'?

12. What port town faces Yarmouth on the Isle of Wight?

13. What film starred Sandra Bullock and Melissa McCarthy?

14. If you have BO people may avoid you. What does BO stand for?

15. Who was the eldest daughter of King James I and VI?

16. The name of what New York street is closely associated with the advertising Industry?

17. What is the official language of Benin?

18. What is a landscape formed from the dissolution of soluble rocks such as limestone, dolomite, and gypsum?

19. Who was Shakespeare's wife?

20. How does the Anaconda kill its prey?

Trivia Time 5

1. Who play at The Bescot?

2. What organisation regulates the broadcasting, telecommunications and postal industries of the United Kingdom?

3. Which middle layer of a tooth contains the root canals?

4. In what state of America is Fort Sumter?

5. Who are the most famous exhibition basketball team?

6. Who was the last Pharaoh?

7. Who starred in *The Rockford Files*?

8. What is the tallest mountain in the world that is not part of the Himalayas or the Andes?

9. Who was Barbara Windsor's gangster husband?

10. What is the largest religious monument in the world?

11. What was John Speed a famous maker of?

12. In which cartoon would you find the character Sideshow Bob?

13. What was Roger Moore's first Bond film?

14. What hypersaline lake lies between Israel and Jordan?

15. What is the most popular car brand (by sales) in Spain?

16. Who provided the original music for the film *Despicable Me*?

17. What is Hormel Foods Corporation's most famous product?

18. What is the most famous Hillbilly Feud?

19. What is the chemical symbol for Mercury?

20. What name is given to the Japanese Mafia?

"Stay out of the black and into the red, nothing in this game for two in a bed."

Trivia Time 6

1. What country does Pope Francis come from?

2. We call the country Cambodia in the West, but what name is more commonly used in the East?

3. Who was the father of Bashar al-Assad?

4. What name is given to bridge structures that carry navigable waterway canals over other rivers, valleys, railways or roads?

5. What country is believed to have the lowest crime rate in the world?

6. What order has the motto 'In Action Faithful and in Honour Clear'?

7. What is the highest rank in the British Army?

"101 or more with 6 darts for tonight's mystery star prize"

8. What department store chain started in 1831 Benjamin Harvey opened a linen shop?

9. What country has the largest army?

10. What was the name of Pink Floyd's 1994 album?

11. In which Indian city is the *Best Exotic Marigold Hotel* located?

12. Who wrote *Oranges Are Not The Only Fruit*?

13. What US state capital took its name from the French for red stick?

14. What was the westernmost gate in London Wall?

15. Where did John Lennon and Yoko Ono go on honeymoon?

16. Moshe Dayan was a military leader and politician in which country?

17. The Santa Clara Valley is located in which US state?

18. Who was the longest serving Prime Minister of the United Kingdom?

19. What is the capital of Libya?

20. What are of London is named after an inn called The Swiss Tavern that was built in 1804 in the style of a Swiss chalet?

Trivia Time 7

1. The Saffir Simpson scale is a scale which classifies the intensities of what?

2. What is Marco Pierre White famous for?

3. What is the anglicised name for the Gaelic May Day festival?

4. Mount Pelée is a volcano on what island?
   Carribean X *Fitzgerald*

5. What was President Kennedy's middle name?

6. What was 'Rambo's' Christian name?

7. Who created Jason Bourne?

"Look at what you could have won."

8. Who was the most famous member of St. Cecile Lodge #568 Masonic Lodge?

9. What city is the second-most populous in Virginia?

10. How long does a Secretary General of the United Nations serve for?

11. In the 1800s who were 'Cousin Jacks'?

12. What Australian fast bowler of the 90s was famous for his Handlebar Moustache?

13. Which continent is the home of the tsetse fly?

14. Who founded Napster?
    Sean Parker ✓

15. On what island would you find the famous Blue Grotto?
    Capri, South Italy ✓

16. What river runs through Shakespeare's birthplace?

17. In what country was Nicole Kidman born?

18. What name is given to a body of water where ships, boats and barges seek shelter from stormy weather, or are stored for future use?

19. Who had a hit with *Romeo and Juliet* in 1981?
    Shakespeare X *Dire Staits*

20. What cartoon character was originally called Happy Rabbit?
    Looney Tunes Bugs Bunny. ✓

Trivia Time 8

1. What title is given to the Queen's personal representative in each county of the United Kingdom?

2. 4 countries which are not members of the European Union use the Euro as their official currency. Name them.

3. What is the phonetic alphabet word for the letter Z?

4. What inert gas gets trapped in the blood when a diver gets the bends?

5. What was the name of Queen Victoria's Summer House on the Isle of Wight?

6. In what year was the first Test Tube Baby born?

7. What is the Southernmost capital city in Europe?

"And Bully's Special Priiiiize..." Time!

8. In what town was Jesus born?

   Bethleham ✓

9. What is the currency of Croatia?

   Croatian kuna ✓

10. In which war did the Third Battle of Gaza take place?

11. What name is given to an ice cream cone with a flake in it?

    Whippy ice Cream ✓

12. What town stands where the rivers Goyt and Tame merge to create the River Mersey?

13. Which Golfer, born in 1870, won The Open five times?

14. Who is the matriarch of the Mitchell family in *Eastenders*?

15. Roadrunners are members of which family of birds?

16. What is Ireland's oldest university?

    Trinity College, Dublin ✓

17. Who was the lead singer of Culture Club?

18. Who was the founder of Amazon?

    Jeff Bezos ✓

19. What word is given to the amount of light an object absorbs?

20. In which year was Queen Victoria crowned?

    1837 ✓

Queen Victoria 18 years old year 1837 Crowned

Trivia Time 9

1. What nationality was Madame Tussaud?

2. What London landmark was closed for repairs soon after it opened?

3. What song from *Slumdog Millionaire* gave a hit for The Pussycat Dolls?

4. How long does a rugby match last?

5. What was the distinguishing feature of Israeli General Moshe Dayan's appearance?

6. Who created *Maigret*?

7. What is the name of *Sherlock Holmes*' Brother?

"Innnnnn eight..."

8. What was the name of Alan Clark MP's home?

9. What is a term for people who dwell in rural, mountainous areas in the United States, primarily in Appalachia?

10. Who created *The Simpsons*?

11. Who does Tottenham play in the North London Derby?

12. What name is given to the annual Islamic pilgrimage to Mecca?

13. In what county was Victoria Beckham born?

14. What is the largest city in Tanzania?

15. Two thirds of the population of what island were forced to flee after a 1995 volcanic eruption?

16. What nationality was Explorer Robery Peary?

17. In what city would you find the most famous street named Reeperbahn?

18. The King Fahd Causeway links Saudia Arabia with which other country?

19. What is the 2nd tallest mountain in Africa?

20. What shape is the famous Weather Vane at Lord's Cricket Ground?

Trivia Time 10

1. In what year did David Beckham marry Victoria Adams?

2. What was the worldwide highest grossing film of 2014?

3. Barack Obama visited Cuba in 2016. When was the last visit by a US President?

4. Where can the Scottish Police Training College be found?

5. In what country was the largest Gold Nugget ever found with a metal detector?

6. Who created the character of *Rupert Bear*?

7. Who was god of the sun in Ancient Egyptian mythology?

8. What is the name of the children's book character created by Julianne Moore?

9. In what year was *Rambo: First Blood* released?

10. Who shows you to your seat at a theatre or a wedding?

11. What do Morphy Richards make?

12. What is the largest church in the world by volume?

13. What name is given to a form of protest in which people congregate outside a place of work or location where an event is taking place?

14. What is the most popular car brand (by sales) in the UK?

15. What is the second largest city in Egypt?

16. The first shots of the US Civil war took place where?

17. What is the religious legal system governing the members of the Islamic faith?

18. How is Cobalamin more commonly known?

19. Who denied Jesus three times?

20. In 2001, which actor took over the flying of his plane, bound for Kenya, and managed to return it to safety?

"You win nothing but your BFH... Bus Fare Home"

Trivia Time 11

1. What is the largest town on Anglesey?

2. Who played the Monster in the 1994 film Mary Shelley's *Frankenstein*?

3. Who created *Family Guy* and *American Dad*?

4. In what year did *Newsround* begin?

5. How many boats passed through the Suez Canal between 1968 and 1974?

6. What river is located along the southern border of Texas?

7. What was the name of John du Pont's wrestling training team?

8. In what town is Osborne House?

"101 or more with 6 darts for tonight's mystery star prize"

9. Which English Football Club's motto is 'To Dare Is to Do'?

10. As of 2016, which Middle Eastern country has the longest serving ruler?

11. Who was the only member of the Forbes 400 richest Americans ever to be convicted of murder?

12. What Indian phrase means 'Let there be Victory'?

13. Which artist, whose work originated in Bristol, has a distinctive stencilling style?

14. Who provided the voice for Mickey Mouse from 1928 to 1946?

15. What comedian's real name is Geoffrey J Rowe?

16. The name of which architectural movement comes from the French word for 'raw'?

17. Which Dutch port gave The Beautiful South a hit?

18. What was Al-Andalus?

19. What name is given to the Chinese Mafia?

20. What is a Tam O'Shanter?

Trivia Time 12

1. What genre of films would you associate with Vincent Price?

2. What country was formerly known as Dahomey?

3. How long does a football match last for?

"All for the throw of a dart"

4. What is the name of *Tintin's* dog?

5. A bridle is a piece of headgear often used to control what animal?

6. Who wrote *The Fall of the House of Usher*?

7. What is the largest of the Canary Islands?

8. According to Forbes Global 2000 2015 list, which company has the highest market value in the world?

9. What is a Motte and Bailey?

10. What Empire existed from 1299 to 1923?

11. What is reputed to have been the final battle of King Arthur?

12. Who was the only British Gold Medal winner at the Sochi Winter Olympics?

13. What seat was held by a member of the Rothschild family from 1865 to 1923?

14. On what day of the year did Harry Houdini die?

15. Where is the original Balfour Declaration kept?

16. Who is the main presenter of *The Last Leg*?

17. What war raged in the Balkans from 28th February 1998 until 1st June 1999?

18. What was the headline on the last ever edition of the *News of the World*?

19. Who was the Leader of the Khmer Rouge regime?

20. What famous actress was born in Fort Bragg?

Trivia Time 13

1. With which book would you associate Norris McWhirter?

2. Who meet each year at the Appleby Horse Fair?

3. The 1969 British Miner's Strike saw the first use of what type of protest action?

4. Who trades as 'DEB' on the London Stock Exchange?

5. What is the driest non-polar desert in the world?

6. Vientiane is the capital of what country?

7. Who painted *The Thin Red Line*?

"Go for your lights"

8. Who resigned as Pope in 2013?

9. What does the prefix Caer mean in Welsh placenames?

10. In the 1970s, what Battle led to the implementation of the 3-Day Week?

11. Who is the main presenter of *Gardener's World*?

12. In what year was actress Kristin Bell born?

13. What type of animal is *Pingu*?

14. What month's birthstone places highest on the Mohs scale?

15. In what field is 'Paddy Power' a well known name?

16. Who was the first Pilot to break the sound barrier?

17. What U is a demand given with a threat following non-compliance?

18. What is the largest bank in the United States?

19. Who played Sean Parker in *The Social Network*?

20. How many countries has Yugoslavia split up into?

Trivia Time 14

1. Where is the Grand National ran?

2. Who was the wife of Pharaoh Akhenaten?

3. What name is given to the Russian Mafia?

4. Who dueted with Freddie Mercury on *Barcelona*?

5. How is a fried breakfast known in Northern Ireland?

"You've got the time it takes for the board to revolve..."

6. What name is given to a monetary system in which the standard economic unit of account is based on a fixed quantity of gold?

7. What is a PDA between lovers?

8. What is the capital of Kenya?

9. What was a B52?

10. Which city's museum was formerly known as Huntly House?

11. What kind of animal is *Bambi*?

12. Who presents *Most Haunted*?

13. What was Operation Chastise?

14. In what 2006 film did Sebastian Foucan, the inventor of free running, show off his sport?

15. What is 'Ye Olde Trip to Jerusalem'?

16. Who is the Chairman, President and CEO of Berkshire Hathaway?

17. Who plays the title character in *Saving Private Ryan*?

18. What is the most common Blood type?

19. In what country is the small town of Hay-on-Wye?

20. Who is the Female Patron Saint of Catalonia?

Trivia Time 15

1. What is the tallest mountain in North America?

2. Margaret Thatcher was involved in the development of which sweet food?

3. Where did Golfer Harry Vardon come from?

4. Which number on the Beaufort Wind Scale represents a storm?

5. What type of Islam is most common in the Kingdom of Jordan?

6. What was the follow-up to the TV series *Life on Mars*?

7. In which area of the United Kingdom is Square Sausage most popular?

8. What kind of animal is Dumbo?

9. What is the Kaaba?

10. What town lies directly across the Mersey from Runcorn?

11. Who is the usual narrator in the *Sherlock Holmes* stories?

12. What are the 3 main types of rock?

13. What is the name of the summer residence of the Pope?

14. What nationality was Herge, the creator of *Tintin*?

15. Who was David Beckham's best man?

16. What British film production company is best known for its Gothic Horror films?

17. What is the capital of Kenya?

18. Who owns the Suez Canal?

19. What is the name of Johan Cruyff's son?

20. Which Welsh cleric popularised the tales of King Arthur?

"101 or more with 6 darts for tonight's mystery star prize"

Trivia Time 16

1. In what London street is the Stock Exchange located?

2. What famous maze is mentioned in *Three Men in a Boat*?

3. Georgina Baillie was at the centre of what controversy?

4. Who ensures discipline in a political party?

5. Who wrote the hymn *What a Friend We Have in Jesus*?

6. What name is given to the native peoples of Greenland, Canada and Alaska?

7. Who is older, Matt Damon or Ben Affleck?

8. Who was the first King of the united Italy?

9. Do Penguins live at the North Pole or the South Pole?

10. Is Gretna in Scotland or England?

11. Is Sean Connery Scottish or Irish?

12. Which organisation has more active personnel, the Indian Navy or the Royal Navy?

13. Did Gandhi and Hitler ever meet?

14. As of 2016, is Little Richard still alive?

15. Is Marijuana legal in North Korea?

16. If an item is a luxury, could it be described as up-market or down-market?

17. Do the Amish use motorized washing machines?

18. Is a Chinook wind hot or cold?

19. What country has the larger population, North Korea or South Korea?

20. Who died a mysterious death in Hong Kong in 1973?

"You can't beat a bit of Bully!"

Trivia Time 17

1. Which actor was nominated for an Academy Award in 1978 but then had to wait until 2013 for his next nomination?

2. Who played *The Horse Whisperer*?

3. What terrible accident happened to Christopher Reeve in 1995?

4. What was Terence Stamp's film debut?

5. How many times was Elizabeth Taylor married?

6. Whose catchphrase was 'Chase me, chase me'?

7. Which comedy character had the catchphrase 'yeah but no but yeah but'?

8. Whose catchphrase was 'ding dong'?

9. Whose catchphrase was 'Ooh! I could crush a grape'?

10. How many keys on a piano?

11. What A might draw up the designs for your house?

12. What J could hang the doors in your house?

13. What O may carry out routine tasks in a hospital?

14. In Greek Mythology who was the dog that never failed to catch whatever it was hunting?

15. Who flew too close to the sun in Greek Mythology?

16. What were slaves called in Ancient Sparta?

17. Who was Charon in Greek Mythology?

18. Which dog guarded the gates of the Underworld?

19. What city was founded by Alexander the great in 331 BC?

20. The ancient city of Tyre is now part of which modern country?

"Let's check that with Bully"

True Crime

1. Which American female found guilty (but later released) of the murder of Meredith Kercher?

2. Who hijacked an Airplane in 1971, robbed the passengers and then escaped via a Parachute?

3. Steve McQueen started carrying a gun at all times due to fear of attack from whom?

4. Which American Union leader vanished in 1975?

5. Which judge oversaw the O.J. Simpson trial?

6. What saying, meaning to do something with unquestionable belief, relates to the Jonestown Massacre?

7. Who were the last people to be hanged in the UK?

8. Which of the Great Train Robbers escaped from Prison in 1965?

"101 or more with 6 darts for tonight's mystery star prize"

9. Who shot Lee Harvey Oswald?

10. Who was the Soham Double Child Murderer?

11. Who was infamously arrested outside Elvis Presley's Graceland home for allegedly intending to shoot him?

12. What name was given to a left-wing revolutionary group responsible for a series of bomb attacks in England between 1970 and 1972?

13. Who was the Yorkshire Ripper's last victim?

14. In which city did Jack the Ripper operate?

15. How do we usually refer to Resurrectionists"?

16. In which country was Joseph Fritzl a resident?

17. What is the capital city of the Central African Republic?

18. The 2008 search for which child turned out to be a hoax instigated by her mother in a search for reward money?

19. What crime was Richard Madeley charged with in 1990?

20. Who was the last woman hanged in Britain?

TV 1

1. Which gameshow was presented by Bruce Forsyth then Matthew Kelly and finally Darren Day?

2. Who is the male presenter of *Total Wipeout*?

3. In which American gameshow must you answer in the form of a question?

4. What gameshow connects John Leslie, Bradley Walsh and Nicky Campbell?

5. Which gameshow was hosted by Jim Davidson and John Virgo?

6. Which gameshow, hosted by David Hamilton, would you try to avoid the stinger?

7. Which show featured Wolf, Nightshade and Jet?

8. The Danish version of which gameshow is called *Man of the Day*?

"The subjects that are lit are the ones you can hit!"

9. Paris Hilton and Nicole Ritchie starred in what Reality show?

10. What item of his anatomy did Rylan Clark have enhanced soon after becoming a famous face on TV?

11. Who is the male star of *Outlander*?

12. What was *Lovejoy's* profession?

13. Who is the youngest ever presenter of Blue Peter?

14. Who is best known as the presenter of *How to look good naked*?

15. What was the character name of the mother in *The Royle Family*?

16. How many episodes of *The Last of the Summer Wine* were made?

17. What TV show features entrepreneurs pitching their business ideas in order to secure investment finance from a panel of venture capitalists?

18. Who is the longest serving presenter of *Blue Peter*?

19. Who played Sue Ellen in *Dallas*?

20. Who played *Lovejoy*?

TV 2

1. What TV show's theme song was entitled *Where Everybody Knows Your Name*?

2. What did UKTV G2 become?

3. Who played Al Capone in the HBO series *Boardwalk Empire*?

4. Which Welsh Presenter has appeared on *The One Show* since 2010?

5. Steven Van Zandt, star of *The Sopranos*, was famously a backing musician for whom?

6. In which TV street could you visit Roy's Rolls?

7. What character was played by Una Stubbs in the *Worzel Gummidge* TV series?

8. In what street might you find Bert, Ernie and Big Bird?

9. Which actor has played Paul Robinson in *Neighbours* for over 20 years (on and off)?

10. Who won the first series of *The X Factor*?

11. In which fictional town did Jessica Fletcher live?

12. Who was the first presenter of *Mock the Week*?

13. Which 2014 TV series stars Vic Reeves, Bob Mortimer and Matt Berry?

14. In which TV sitcom does the character Super Hans appear?

15. Who have been the judges on *The Great British Bake Off* since it began?

16. Who was *The Naked Chef*?

17. Who played *The Naked Civil Servant*?

18. In which TV show would you meet Mulder and Scully?

19. Which popular early 90s TV show started off with the discovery of a body wrapped in plastic?

20. Which TV series, beginning in 2004, had one of the most expensive pilot episodes ever?

"All for the throw of a dart"

TV 3

1. The last series of which TV show still holds the American viewing figures record?

2. What is TV Show *Strictly Come Dancing* called in the USA?

3. What fictional village was *All Creatures Great and Small* set?

4. Who was KITT's arch enemy?

5. Who played Tonto in the TV series *The Lone Ranger*?

6. In what year was Bruce Forsyth born?

"You've had a good night out - but you go home with nowt!"

7. Who wrote the TV series *Lipstick on Your Collar*?

8. Who has presented *Watchdog, Countryfile* and *Wainwrights Walks*?

9. What controversial incident meant the end for Jeremy Clarkson on *Top Gear*?

10. Who succeeded Anneka Rice on *Treasure Hunt*?

11. In which smash 80s comedy were David and Maddy the main characters?

12. Who has presented *Take Me Out* since it began?

13. Which creator and writer brought us *Two and a Half Men* and *The Big Bang Theory*?

14. Who is the oldest judge on the 2016 UK series of *The Voice*?

15. What TV Detective's first name was Endeavour?

16. What is the name of Sky's flagship Football results programme on Saturday Afternoon's?

17. Which 'Friend' joined the presenting team on *Top Gear*?

18. Who was the founder and first president of the National Viewers' and Listeners' Association?

19. What sketch troupe comprised Newman, Baddiel, Punt and Dennis?

20. What early 90s costume drama featured two sisters starting their own fashion house?

TV 4

1. In what year was *Sesame Street* first shown?

2. Who is the Father in the *Addam's Family*?

3. What was piloted by Vietnam veteran Stringfellow Hawke?

4. In which show are contestants rated on how well they host a dinner party?

"Throwers and Knowers"

5. On which TV station is *Celebrity Juice* broadcast?

6. What Saturday morning show did the BBC air between 1987 and 1993?

7. Who played *John Adams* in the Award-Winning Mini Series?

8. *The Teletubbies* consisted of Tinky Winky, Laa-Laa, Dipsy and who else?

9. Who played Monk in *Monk*?

10. What was the nickname of Jimmy Nail's character in *Auf Wiedersehen, Pet*?

11. Daphne Fowler is a member of which TV team?

12. Who was the long time presenter of *Fifteen to One*?

13. Which Hulk actor appeared in *King of Queens*?

14. Who were the two presenters of *Hole in the Wall*?

15. Who played Burke in *Taggart*?

16. What TV station gave us *Ax Men* and *Pawn Stars*?

17. Who won Series One of *Strictly Come Dancing*?

18. What was the name of the fictional holiday camp in *Hi-de-Hi!*?

19. How did Tyrion Lannister kill his father in *Game of Thrones*?

20. In what year was Channel 5 launched?

TV 5

1. In what TV series was John Anderson the main referee?

2. What TV show featured celebrities as they try to master the art of diving?

3. What *This Morning* presenter had her big break on *Blind Date*?

4. Who created *Fraggle Rock*?

5. How many people are on each team in *University Challenge*?

6. Who did Phillip Schofield replace on *This Morning*?

7. Who played Quentin Crisp in the TV film *The Naked Civil Servant*?

8. Which male dancer from Grimsby is a *Strictly* favourite?

9. Who defeated Susan Boyle in *Britain's Got Talent*?

10. Harold Bishop was a long-term character in what soap?

"101 or more with 6 darts for tonight's mystery star prize"

11. Which comedy character revived *Through the Keyhole* in the 2010s?

12. Who was the original host of *MasterChef*?

13. Who was one of the female stars of *The Good Life*?

14. Who produced the theme tune to *Moonlighting*?

15. RT is a popular news channel. What does RT stand for?

16. Which series gave Ant and Dec their big break?

17. Who was Mulder and Scully's Boss in *The X-Files*?

18. Who hosts *Only Connect*?

19. What is the name of Samantha's daughter in *Bewitched*?

20. How many series of *Downton Abbey* were made?

TV 6

1. What was the name of the British remake of *The Golden Girls*?

2. Sandy and Sandra are well known faces on which TV programme?

3. What role is most closely associated with Peter Falk?

4. Which 2011 US TV series was based on the Israeli series *Hafufim*?

5. Which character was the leader in *The A-Team*?

6. Who played Rab C. Nesbitt for many years?

7. Which 1998 to 2000 sitcom was written by Craig Cash and Caroline Aherne?

8. Which TV characters live on Wimbledon Common?

9. What connects Christopher Biggins, Tony Blackburn and Carol Thatcher?

10. In *Eastenders* who was the father of Ricky, Janine and Diane?

11. In which TV show was Terry McCann the title character?

12. Which actor gave us the *Mr Tumble* character?

13. Which Sky channel is known for mostly transmitting game shows?

14. Who presented *Changing Rooms*?

15. Which DIY programme has Nick Knowles hosted since 1999?

16. Who played the Medical Examiner *Quincy*?

17. Who presented *Countdown* for 23 years?

18. Who was the misanthropic Doctor played by Hugh Laurie?

19. Carl and Susan are at the head of what family in *Neighbours*?

20. Which TV channel gave us *The IT Crowd*?

"Stay out of the black and into the red, nothing in this game for two in a bed."

UK Places

1. In which UK city does Stanley Park separate the homes of the two main Football clubs?

2. What is the nickname for Liverpool's Catholic Cathedral?

3. What name is often given to the manuscript of the *Great Survey* carried out by William the Conqueror?

4. Which Hampshire town is known as the 'Home of the British Army'?

5. What is the nearest town to Manchester Airport?

6. Where in Britain would you find 'The Theatre by the Lake'?

7. What is the British town to feature in the name of a Shakespeare play?

"Now the cash you won for charity earlier... that's safe."

8. In which British town are the headquarters of the open university?

9. Where was the first new town in Britain?

10. According to the University of Buckingham, what is the oldest town in Britain?

11. The name of which Welsh town means Crow Valley?

12. Near which town was the Flying Scotsman derailed during the General Strike?

13. How many times is it said that Berwick Upon Tweed has changed hands between Scotland and England?

14. Which city is regarded as the Capital of the Scottish Highlands?

15. Near which town does the River Ribble meet the sea?

16. In which Norfolk village did a Saxon noblewoman have a vision of the Virgin Mary in 1061?

17. In which Scottish town was IRN-BRU invented?

18. Which town has been represented by Dennis Skinner since 1970?

19. In which British town did a bomb kill 31 people in August 1998?

20. What is the biggest town on the Isle of Wight?

USA 1

1. What is the smallest US State by area?

2. In what state can Disney World be found?

3. What is the name of the famous former prison in San Francisco Bay?

4. What is the United States oldest institution of Higher Learning?

5. Which American created *Wheel of Fortune* and *Jeopardy!*?

"Super, smashing, great."

6. Edgar Allan Poe died in which city?

7. Which American city has the slogan, 'The West's Most Western Town'?

8. What was Butch Cassidy's real name?

9. In what year was *The Star Spangled Banner* designated as the US National Anthem?

10. In 1853, what country sold the US land, in what was known as the Gadsden Purchase?

11. In which US state is Shenandoah National Park located?

12. What is the name of the US Military Academy in Orange County, New York?

13. How many institutions make up the Ivy League?

14. In what year did the notorious Waco Seige occur?

15. In which US State would you find the Black Hills?

16. Which Texas city is the 4th most populous in the United States?

17. Near what major US city is Ellis Island located?

18. What is the name of obelisk which stands in the National Mall, Washington DC?

19. Who wrote *Roots*?

20. What name is used to described the 1973 landmark court decision on abortion law?

USA 2

1. Which large American city was founded by Antoine de la Mothe Cadillac?

2. The mouth of what bay is located between Cape Charles and Cape Henry?

3. What shape is the Luxor Hotel in Las Vegas?

4. What US city is 'The City that Care Forgot'?

5. Waxahachie is a town in what state?

6. Which area of New York derives from 'South of Houston Street'?

7. What area of Manhattan is centred around Mulberry Street?

8. What is the largest in area of the five boroughs of New York City?

"Innnnnn one..."

9. In which city does *Pawn Stars* take place?

10. What New York school is widely regarded as one of the world's leading music schools?

11. What is the capital of the American state of Nevada?

12. Which American evangelical Christian evangelist was a spiritual adviser to Nixon and Eisenhower amongst others?

13. In what year did the 9/11 attacks take place?

14. What is the largest city in the Mojave Desert in the USA?

15. What is the capital city of the U.S. state of California?

16. In which US city is the Sears Tower?

17. In which decade was the Empire State Building completed?

18. What do Americans traditionally eat on Thanksgiving?

19. In which city did the attack on Rodney King by police spark extensive riots in 1992?

20. Which is the northernmost of the five boroughs of New York City?

War

1. What was the name of the plane that dropped the atomic bomb on Hiroshima?

2. The Vietnam Ware ended with the fall of what city in 1975?

3. What is a Kalashnikov?

4. Which North Vietnamese Army leader died in 1969?

5. Where would you find Anderson shelters in WW2?

6. What treaty ended the American Revolution?

"You win nothing but your BFH... Bus Fare Home"

7. Which country had the largest Battleships of WW2?

8. What year is sometimes known as the year of revolution?

9. Where did the Big 3 Leaders meet in February 1945?

10. The Battle of Spion Kop was fought in which war?

11. How long did the Hundred Years' War last?

12. Who defeated the Polish Army in 1241?

13. What War ran from 1947 to 1991?

14. In what country was Osama bin Laden born?

15. In World War 2, the streets were patrolled by the ARP. What does ARP stand for?

16. In what year of WWI were the RAF formed?

17. What was the first Major battle of WWI?

18. Who commanded the British Fleet in the Battle of Jutland?

19. Which war is featured in the film *Full Metal Jacket*?

20. Which battle ended the Axis threat to Egypt?

Who Was Born First?

1. Who was born first Holly Willoughby or Fearne Cotton?

2. Who was born first Jeremy Corbyn or Tony Blair?

3. Who was born first Nigel Mansell or Ayrton Senna?

4. Who was born first Adolf Hitler or Winston Churchill?

5. Who was born first Donald Trump or Bill Clinton?

6. Who was born first Ronald Reagan or Richard Nixon?

7. Who was born first Prince William or Kate Middleton?

8. Who was born first Richard Branson or Alan Sugar?

9. Who was born first Gary Lineker or Diego Maradona?

10. Who was born first Freddie Mercury or David Bowie?

11. Who was born first Wayne Rooney or Jade Goody?

12. Who was born first Myra Hindley or Ian Brady?

13. Who was born first Miley Cyrus or Justin Bieber?

14. Who was born first Bruce Forsyth or Queen Elizabeth II?

15. Who was born first Hulk Hogan or Gordon Brown?

16. Who was born first Jamie Oliver or Katie Price?

17. Who was born first Larry Hagman or Muhammad Ali?

18. Who was born first John Travolta or Olivia Newton-John?

19. Who was born first Vincent Van Gogh or JMW Turner?

20. Who was born first Hugh Laurie or Stephen Fry?

"Go for your lights"

WW2

1. Who was the leader of Chinese Nationalist forces in WW2?

2. Which date would go down in infamy according to FDR?

3. What was the code name for the Normandy landings?

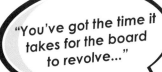

"You've got the time it takes for the board to revolve..."

4. What title, meaning Leader, was used by Hitler?

5. What colourful title was used to describe the Soviet Army?

6. Who was the ceremonial chief of the Waffen SS?

7. What is the German word for 'Lightning War'?

8. Which German operation of 1944 caused US forces to incur their highest casualties for any operation during the war?

9. Which island was invaded by the Germans on 20th May 1941?

10. Who was the leader of Axis Italy during WW2?

11. What was the '20th July Plot'?

12. Where did Rudolf Hess fly to in a possible attempt to broker a peace deal?

13. How are the first 8 months of WW2 often referred to as?

14. In 1939 legislation was enacted to conscript men between what age ranges?

15. Complete the WW2 poster saying, 'Loose Lips...'?

16. Which forces, fighting with the British throughout WW2, were not invited to the VE Day celebrations?

17. Which British India special force were formed to operate deep behind Japanese lines?

18. Where was the capital of unoccupied France from 1940 to 1944?

19. What was the only part of the British Commonwealth to be occupied by Germany in WW2?

20. In what year did Rudolf Hess die?

Answers

2000s Music

1 Colourblind
2 *Patience*
3 Lisa Left Eye Lopes
4 Joe McElderry
5 Avril Lavigne
6 Craig David
7 *The Importance of Being Idle*
8 *Do you really like it?*
9 *Umbrella*
10 Shakira's *Hips don't lie*
11 The Arctic Monkeys
12 David Sneddon
13 Dappy, Tulisa and Fazer
14 2001
15 Dido
16 Westlife
17 Jack the Lad Swing
18 OMD
19 Steps
20 The Ting Tings

PG. 6

50/50

1 Yes
2 Sheffield
3 East Coast
4 Declan Donnelly
5 Right
6 South
7 Canada
8 Lorraine Kelly
9 Chuck Norris
10 Mouse
11 Boris Johnson
12 Israel
13 Scotsman
14 Yes
15 Real Madrid
16 Cambridge
17 Over 1000
18 Stan Laurel
19 Al Pacino
20 Yes

PG. 7

60s Music

1 *Move Over Darling*
2 Mary Hopkins
3 Lonnie Donegan
4 Apple
5 The Shadows
6 Chubby Checker
7 *Strangers in the night*
8 Ken Dodd
9 Adam Faith
10 The Kinks
11 1
12 *Hit the Road, Jack*
13 *Stranger on the Shore*
14 *From Me to You*
15 *Born to be Wild*
16 Wendy Richards
17 *Green, Green Grass of Home*
18 Engelbert Humperdinck
19 The Beach Boys
20 Gary Puckett & The Union Gap

PG. 8

Answers

80s Music

1 *Hole In My Shoe*
2 The Guildford Stranglers
3 George Michael
4 *Is There Something I Should Know?* Duran Duran
5 34
6 The Power Station
7 *Do They Know It's Christmas* by Band Aid II
8 T'Pau
9 A Trio
10 Steve Strange
11 Duran Duran
12 *Two Tribes* by Frankie Goes to Hollywood
13 Sam Fox and Mick Fleetwood
14 Freddie Mercury
15 Susannah Hoffs
16 *Golden Brown* by The Stranglers
17 *Manic Monday*
18 Holly Johnson
19 *Touch Me (I want your body)*
20 *Sexual Healing*

PG. 9

Abbreviations

1 Orenthal James
2 Financial Times Stock Exchange
3 United States of America
4 Follow Friday
5 John Ronald Reuel
6 Palestine Liberation Organization
7 Video Home System
8 John Ross
9 Frederik Willem
10 Pamela Lyndon
11 Herbert George
12 To Be Honest
13 Deoxyribonucleic acid
14 In My Opinion
15 Crime Scene Investigation
16 In Case You Missed It
17 Joseph Mallard William
18 Orchestral Manoeuvres in the Dark
19 Union of Soviet Socialist Republics
20 University and Colleges Admissions Services

PG. 10

Actors

1 Adrien Brody
2 Harry Connick Jnr
3 Jamie Farr
4 Peachy Carnehan
5 *Edward Scissorhands*
6 Guy Siner
7 Peter Dinklage
8 *Kramer vs Kramer*
9 Joe Mantegna
10 South Africa
11 Thomas Cruise Mapother IV
12 Leonardo di Caprio
13 Dolph Lundgren
14 Michael Douglas
15 *Wall Street*
16 Brandon and Shannon
17 Harry Palmer
18 Laurence Olivier
19 Sam Malone
20 Hyman Roth

PG. 11

Answers

Actresses

1. Robert Wagner and Christopher Walken
2. Tom Cruise
3. Zooey Deschanel
4. Kelly McGillis
5. Virginia Madsen
6. Katherine Hepburn
7. Kirke
8. Glenn Close
9. *High Society*
10. Sandra Dee
11. Caemron Diaz
12. Bette Davis
13. Maureen O'Sullivan
14. Vivien Leigh
15. Thalia Shire
16. Oman
17. Justin Theroux
18. Katniss Everdine
19. Daryl Hannah
20. Street Fighter

PG. 12

Americanisms

1. Recess
2. Faucet
3. Cellphone
4. A Clerk
5. Sticking his fingers up at someone
6. Pacifier
7. The Redeye
8. Trunk
9. Skeet Shooting
10. Period
11. Checkers
12. Mortuary
13. Diapers
14. Cilantro
15. Pants
16. Mom or Mommy
17. Public School
18. They also call that "Gas"
19. Pavement
20. Parking Lot

PG. 13

Animals 1

1. Moose (or Elk)
2. Hen
3. Breaching
4. Elephant
5. The Bald Eagle
6. Lamb
7. Diurnal
8. Hands
9. A Bear
10. A Jenny
11. 3
12. No tail
13. 4
14. Ursine
15. St Bernard
16. Ostrich
17. Coyote
18. Marsupial
19. Giant Tortoise
20. The Red Book

PG. 14

Answers

Animals 2

1	Polar Bear	12	Common snapping turtle
2	Hibernation	13	Wolf
3	Owls	14	Squirrels
4	The Dandie Terrier	15	Green Anaconda
5	Drake	16	Cormorant
6	18	17	Ears
7	Hatchling	18	Tripe
8	Bitch	19	Fish
9	Orca	20	Doe
10	Pup		
11	Holt		

PG. 15

Anything Goes 1

1	March or Die'	10	Kindles
2	Mittens	11	Anorak
3	24	12	Lana Turner
4	In a police station	13	36D
5	The Order of the Solar Temple	14	Lesotho
6	The Eagles	15	At sea
7	When hair is pulled back tightly and tied in a bun or ponytail at the back.	16	Lee Harvey Oswald
		17	New York Yankees
8	Tie knots	18	The Ku Klux Klan
9	Larry Bird	19	1995
		20	*The Zapruder film*

PG. 16

Anything Goes 2

1	Frederick Austerlitz	11	Pointed Shoes
2	Tinder	12	Beard
3	81	13	Liberty, Equality, Fraternity
4	The Protocols of the Elders of Zion	14	On his face, they are spectacles
5	Nebraska	15	Olof Palme
6	A necktie with wide pointed wings, similar to a cravat	16	Seattle
		17	Samsung
7	Make America Great Again	18	Wiki Leaks
8	Tweed	19	Susannah Constantine
9	Donkey Jacket	20	Rita Hayworth
10	Kim Dotcom		

PG. 17

Answers

Anything Goes 3

1 In God We Trust
2 The Police
3 That Obama was ineligible as President as he was born overseas
4 Marlene Dietrich
5 I'll finally get to see Marilyn'
6 On your hands
7 16
8 Jodie Foster
9 Cracker
10 David Icke
11 Be Prepared
12 Greta Garbo
13 Sonic the Hedgehog
14 Nehru Jacket
15 Silk Road
16 Taxis
17 Getting drunk
18 33
19 Speak to someone (phone)
20 MH370

PG. 18

Bits and Pieces 1

1 1795
2 New York
3 Serbian
4 Rudolph Valentino
5 A container or room in which the bones of dead people are placed.
6 Berwick Upon Tweed
7 Kim Jong-un
8 Earthquakes
9 Caffeine
10 Michael Cimino
11 *Alice's Adventures in Wonderland*
12 William Pitt the Younger
13 Gold, Frankincence and Myrrh
14 Hexagon
15 David Fincher
16 *My Guy*
17 After the War
18 Great Dane
19 Chris Columbus
20 Nylon

PG. 19

Bits and Pieces 2

1 An Earthquake
2 Green
3 *The Last Tycoon*
4 France
5 Canada
6 None
7 Motorbike accident
8 *Thanks for the Memory*
9 HarperCollins
10 1000
11 Pakistan
12 Elephant
13 Uranus
14 1922
15 Sol
16 Ripley
17 Laika
18 A64
19 Kelsey Grammer
20 Roman Polanski

PG. 20

Answers

Bits and Pieces 3

1 Michael Buerk
2 Liver
3 Kenya
4 Bing Crosby
5 Voice Box
6 Amarillo
7 Joe Calzaghe
8 Lewis Carroll
9 Herman's Hermits
10 California
11 Feather
12 Alexander Fleming
13 New Mexico
14 Al Gore
15 One which ceases and then come on again
16 *Taken*
17 2008
18 Barry George
19 *Paranormal Activity*
20 The Dutch Wars of Independence

PG. 21

Bits and Pieces 4

1 John Gotti
2 The Great White Shark
3 *Tangled*
4 Lionel Richie
5 Saint Etienne
6 A Bar
7 *Guy Mannering*
8 Neptune
9 Croquet
10 Water lilies
11 Bat Mitzvah
12 Zambia
13 Traditional horse-drawn wagon used by British Romani people
14 Leo Tolstoy
15 *Peanuts*
16 Rob Ford
17 Ambrosia
18 Portugal
19 Zirhan Zirhan
20 10

PG. 22

Bits and Pieces 5

1 Central Station
2 Lake Maggiore
3 Maundy Thursday
4 Gail Borden
5 Richard Hauptmann
6 Humidor
7 Judge Ito
8 California
9 3
10 Perth
11 Paula Hawkins
12 Tea
13 Charles Dickens
14 Italy
15 A railway station
16 Electrical Resistance
17 The Liberator
18 Rodgers and Hart
19 St Helier
20 Blacksmiths

PG. 23

Answers

Bits and Pieces 6

1	Breech	11	Latin America
2	Vermont	12	Harvey Smith
3	David Lloyd George	13	2
4	Jafar	14	New Zealand
5	Sailors	15	-40
6	Aberdeen	16	*The Valleys*
7	Scotland Yard	17	1926
8	Humidity	18	Wyoming
9	Jeremy Paxman	19	Red
10	Machine Gun	20	Diana Ross

PG. 24

Bits and Pieces 7

1	*Making a Murderer*	12	Jason Manford
2	Cerberus	13	*Saturday Night Fever*
3	Miss Piggy	14	Lizzie Borden
4	Iceland	15	Stan Lee
5	The Foreshore	16	A gambling game played with two dice
6	1980	17	Schnorbitz
7	Idina Menzel	18	The Ionian Islands
8	Waverley	19	*Carry on at your Convenience*
9	Ernest Hemingway	20	*The Jungle Book*
10	Captain Flint		
11	Large tent		

PG. 25

Bits and Pieces 8

1	Bournemouth	11	Tariffs
2	George C. Scott	12	Nitrogen
3	George Oldfield	13	Wind Chill Factor
4	Cheech and Chong	14	Law
5	Saint Etienne	15	Dame Nellie Melba
6	1170	16	1979
7	1759	17	Michelangelo
8	Carlisle	18	Saturnalia
9	Laurie Metcalf	19	Christopher Lee
10	Jack the Dripper	20	Paris

PG. 26

Answers

Bits and Pieces 9

1 Large deciduous tree
2 Bruce Willis
3 Lucifer
4 BBC
5 2011
6 6
7 International Red Cross
8 The Old Bailey
9 Lancashire
10 *Apocalypse Now*
11 Dan Conner
12 Berkeley Square
13 Arthur Conan-Doyle
14 Tim Burton
15 Leuven
16 Lusitania
17 Drumcree
18 Turkish Delight
19 Bovril
20 Ben Affleck and Matt Damon

PG. 27

Bits and Pieces 10

1 He crashed his car into a tree
2 Herman Melville
3 Charlotte
4 Cecil Rhodes
5 Bob Hope
6 John Cazale
7 Helium
8 Spain and Portugal
9 Lemonade
10 Essex
11 A performance art in which participants called cosplayers wear costumes and fashion accessories to represent a specific character
12 Let's get out of here!'
13 Ronin
14 Autoroute
15 Blue
16 Macchiavelli
17 Gallows
18 Red Rose
19 Charcoal
20 The Cutty Sark

PG. 28

Bits and Pieces 11

1 Dopey
2 Cars
3 In a ski-ing accident
4 Modern day USA
5 Brussels
6 66 years
7 *Who framed Roger Rabbit*
8 Jennie Bond
9 Boston
10 Electrons
11 Holmes to Watson
12 Piper Alpha
13 Waterloo
14 Ghana
15 The BeeGees
16 Moors
17 The Sistine Chapel
18 1869
19 Richard Nixon
20 Liverpool

PG. 29

Answers

Bits and Pieces 12

1	Algeria	11	Nitrogen
2	St Andrew	12	Kitten
3	*Toast*	13	Dorothy
4	Ta Ta For Now	14	Peter O'Toole
5	Donna Air	15	John Muir
6	Brain of Britain	16	Bob Monkhouse
7	Old Blood and Guts	17	The Stone of Destiny
8	A40	18	India
9	Jules Verne	19	Edward Heath
10	1961	20	Miloš Forman

PG. 30

Bits and Pieces 13

1	Casus belli	11	The South Pole
2	*Eyes Wide Shut*	12	Nationwide Building Society
3	Beekeper	13	Joan of Arc
4	Princess Margaret	14	Ken Russell
5	1997	15	The Seychelles
6	President Paul Kruger	16	A fish
7	Corfu	17	Shark
8	*Ring Ring*	18	Michael Jackson
9	Swindon	19	Keratin
10	Wolfgang	20	President James Monroe

PG. 31

Bits and Pieces 14

1	King	11	Belfast
2	Albigensian Crusade	12	*Harry Potter and the Philosopher's Stone*
3	167		
4	2 and 3	13	France
5	David Jason	14	Leighton Buzzard
6	Snow	15	Gawker
7	Beefeaters	16	Trabant
8	Jon Voight	17	Zimbabwe
9	Canadian	18	Blue Moon
10	Amityville	19	Lord Cardigan
		20	Joel Chandler Harris

PG. 32

Answers

Bits and Pieces 15

1   Cello
2   The Investigation of the Yorkshire Ripper
3   8
4   Drumlanrig Castle
5   Waterloo Station
6   *The Mona Lisa*
7   No new taxes'
8   Mead
9   Alfred
10 Temple Meads
11 *The Count of Monte Cristo*
12 Grant Wood
13 Tarsus
14 Lewis Carroll
15 Grand Union Canal
16 Speak multiple languages
17 Edinburgh
18 Sinology
19 The Sorbonne
20 Noël Coward

PG. 33

Bits and Pieces 16

1   Harry Gordon Selfridge
2   Piedmont
3   Alchemy
4   David Broome
5   Snake
6   St Jude
7   HG Wells
8   Bernard Cribbins
9   Essex
10 Ariel
11 The Flying Scotsman
12 Everton
13 John Glenn
14 Katie Holmes
15 Glasgow
16 Hokkaido
17 The Tropic of Capricorn
18 Diamonds
19 The California Gold Rush
20 Barry Gibb

PG. 34

Bits and Pieces 17

1   USA
2   Vietnam
3   Clue
4   Pineapple Dance Studios
5   2006
6   Tea Clipper
7   South Yorkshire
8   Ludwig
9   Roger Milla
10 7-Up
11 Rutland
12 Yellow
13 Jake Gyllenhaal
14 6
15 Newcastle
16 No
17 Charlie Brooker
18 Chelmsford
19 Clementine
20 River Brain

PG. 35

Answers

Bits and Pieces 18

1	Pet Detective	11	Akhenaten
2	Mungo Park	12	1807
3	David Livingstone	13	Oliver Cromwell
4	1994	14	1989
5	Winchester Cathedral	15	Napoleon Bonaparte
6	Marquess of Queensberry	16	St. Helena
7	AD79	17	Highgate
8	Treaty of Paris	18	*Just Dance*
9	AD43	19	Ricky Valance
10	Edwin Lutyens	20	Otis Redding

PG. 36

Bits and Pieces 19

1	Kim Carnes	11	Republica
2	3	12	The Apollo Theatre
3	*Grange Hill*	13	Shaftesbury Avenue
4	Billy Joel	14	*The Last Supper*
5	Shakin' Stevens	15	*The Comedy of Errors*
6	The Travelling Wilburys	16	Dadaism
7	Jason Donovan	17	Bosch
8	*Jessie*	18	Sculpture
9	Melanie Chisholm	19	*The Turner Prize*
10	The Rednex	20	Tate Modern

PG. 37

Bits and Pieces 20

1	The Renaissance	11	Geronimo
2	Damien Hirst	12	Maine
3	Charles Rennie Mackintosh	13	Missouri
4	Paris	14	South Carolina
5	Terry Nation	15	Kentucky
6	Roy Walker	16	Boston
7	*Total Wipeout*	17	Liberty Enlightening the World
8	*Celebrity Squares*	18	Theodore Roosevelt
9	William G. Stewart	19	Carson City
10	*The Crystal Maze*	20	New York

PG. 38

Answers

Book First Lines

1 *Pride and Prejudice*
2 *The Great Gatsby*
3 *Moby Dick*
4 Peter, Susan, Edmond, and Lucy
5 *Angela's Ashes*
6 *Brighton Rock*
7 *1984*
8 *Dune*
9 *David Copperfield*
10 *The Grapes of Wrath*
11 *To Kill a Mockingbird*
12 *David Copperfield*
13 *The Cat in the Hat*
14 *The Da Vinci Code*
15 *Peter Pan*
16 *Alice's Adventure in Wonderland*
17 *Dracula*
18 *Throw Momma From the Train*
19 'It was the best of times, it was the worst of times'
20 *Little Women*

PG. 39

Books 1

1 *Treasure Island*
2 CS Lewis
3 Stephen King
4 Neil Gaiman
5 Robert Langdon
6 Victor Hugo
7 Agatha Christie
8 Louis Spence
9 Slaughterhouse Five
10 Agatha Christie
11 Horror
12 Eli Wallach
13 Professor Moriarty
14 Henry Fielding
15 Peter Falk
16 Emily Bronte
17 Edgar Allan Poe
18 Katherine Jenkins
19 Edinburgh
20 David Hasselhoff

PG. 40

Books 2

1 Jilly Cooper
2 Belinda Carlisle
3 Mark Weir
4 Adult Colouring Books
5 Jules Verne
6 Sarah Silverman
7 David Niven
8 Mickey Dolenz
9 *The Hunger Games*
10 Sancho Panza
11 Danny
12 Anastasia Steele
13 *Bleak House*
14 Steve Martin
15 *Roots*
16 *The Man in the High Castle*
17 Barack Obama
18 Ian Fleming
19 Mario Puzo
20 *Anna Karenina*

PG. 41

Answers

Books 3

1 Rudyard Kipling
2 Michael Caine
3 *The Prime of Miss Jean Brodie*
4 JK Rowling
5 Samuel
6 Oz
7 Thomas Hughes
8 Tori Spelling
9 EL James
10 James
11 The Artful Dodger
12 Herman Melville
13 Kindred
14 Adolf Hitler
15 Edgar Rice Burroughs
16 Leopold Bloom
17 *Zorro*
18 Lucy Maud Montgomery
19 *The Secret Garden*
20 Lance Armstrong

PG. 42

Books 4

1 Cervantes
2 Salman Rushdie
3 Michael Crichton
4 2003
5 Joseph Conrad
6 Jonathan Gash
7 Arnold Schwazenegger
8 Dick Francis
9 1997
10 Shane Ritchie
11 The White Rabbit
12 Stella Gibbons
13 Richard Branson
14 2005
15 Judith Kerr
16 Harper Lee never married
17 Conan the Barbarian
18 Roger Moore
19 Lemuel
20 AA Milne

PG. 43

Brilliant Bills

1 Ringo Starr
2 William Cody
3 Bill Gates
4 Bill Bailey
5 Ted Levine
6 *The Hobbit*
7 Bill Maher
8 Bill Oddie
9 Bill Owen
10 Bill Maynard
11 Bill Kenwright
12 Bill Murray
13 Bill Clinton
14 Bill Forsyth
15 Bill Hicks
16 Bill Haley
17 Bill Beaumont
18 Bill Bryson
19 Alcoholics Anonymous
20 Bill Paxton

PG. 44

Answers

Business 1

1 Tesco
2 A mortgage
3 Kellogg
4 Safeway
5 Jack Cohen
6 B&Q
7 Prestatyn
8 Bill Gates
9 Betting Shops
10 Raleigh Cycles
11 Rochester, New York
12 London Interbank Offered Rate
13 South Korea
14 Nick Leeson
15 La Senza
16 Sausages
17 Barclaycard
18 Peter Stringfellow
19 The Sony Walkman
20 Tesco

PG. 45

Business 2

1 Argos
2 Wilko
3 Iceland
4 Radio Rentals
5 Marks and Spencers
6 Hewlett-Packard
7 Unilever
8 Panasonic
9 The Coal Exchange, Cardiff
10 Sweden
11 Steel
12 Tea and Coffee
13 Flour
14 Carrefour
15 Stock Exchange
16 Tyres
17 2009
18 Michelle Mone
19 Mark Zuckerberg
20 Tim Cook

PG. 46

Capital Cities

1 Reykjavík
2 Berlin
3 Santo Domingo
4 Nicosia
5 Belgrade
6 Pristina
7 San Juan
8 Caracas
9 Wellington
10 Kiev
11 Panama City
12 Juba
13 Kathmandu
14 Dhaka
15 Monrovia
16 Tokyo
17 Dublin
18 New Delhi
19 Gaborone
20 The Gambia

PG. 47

Answers

Catchphrases

1	Bugs Bunny	11	Book 'em Danno'
2	Frank Spencer	12	Harry Callahan
3	*Dad's Army*	13	Ken Dood
4	Alan Partridge	14	Victor Meldrew
5	Paul Daniels	15	Les Dennis
6	Tony Blair	16	George Formby
7	Harold Steptoe	17	D'Oh!'
8	*Supermarket Sweep*	18	David Dickinson
9	Come on Down!'	19	Dalek
10	Ali G	20	Tommy Cooper

PG. 48

Comedy

1	Surbiton	11	Mr Hedges
2	Grace Brothers	12	Sportswriter
3	*Shooting Stars*	13	*Frasier*
4	David Brent	14	Howard Cunningham
5	Geraldine McQueen	15	Michelle Dotrice
6	Woody Allen	16	Roy Chubby Brown
7	Stephen Colbert	17	Jim Moir
8	Ronnie Barker	18	Max Headroom
9	Andrew Maxwell	19	*Don't Drink the Water*
10	Graham Linehan	20	The Two Ronnies

PG. 49

Curious Questions 1

1	Protons, Neutrons and Electrons	11	Thomas Jefferson
2	The Rust Belt	12	An Embarassment
3	Frank and Joe	13	TLC
4	Eternia	14	ZTT
5	20	15	Supermassive Black Hole
6	Gary Neville	16	Alfred
7	Scott Baio	17	Chester Racecourse (1m If)
8	Poundland	18	Bette Davis
9	Katie Hopkins	19	John McEnroe
10	Cruella De Vil	20	Michael Finnegan

PG. 50

Answers

Curious Questions 2

1	Barack Obama	11	Five Gold Rings
2	Biotechnology	12	Kazakhstan
3	Bluebell	13	Married
4	Missy Elliot	14	Anchorage
5	Manchester	15	*Hamlet*
6	Portland Stone	16	Hollywoodland
7	Dick Fosbury	17	Nigel Lythgoe
8	Clarinet	18	San Francisco
9	New York	19	Police Officer
10	Cumulonimbus	20	Malibu

PG. 51

Curious Questions 3

1	Fred Elliot	11	George Lucas
2	Milwaukee	12	Zebedee
3	Barrs	13	Reuters
4	Parasol	14	Ghanaian
5	Tintern Abbey	15	Keystone
6	Go for the Juggler	16	*She'll be coming round the mountain*
7	British Academy of Film and Television Art	17	William McKinley
8	Jack/ Jacques	18	Uterus
9	Famous Hypnotist and Motivator	19	The Puritans
10	1970	20	Hanna Barbera

PG. 52

Curious Questions 4

1	1986	11	Tatum O' Neal
2	General Certificate of Secondary Education	12	Thomas
3	Brussels	13	The Stirling Prize
4	Hercules	14	Harry Hamlin
5	Charlaine Harris	15	She drowned herself
6	Edam	16	Dumfries and Galloway
7	Albert	17	Genetics
8	Monica Lewinsky	18	Lays
9	Simon Legree	19	Stevie Winwood
10	Hypocrisy	20	Boxing Day

PG. 53

Answers

Curious Questions 5

1 1956
2 James Joyce
3 Ban Ki-Moon
4 Nigel Farage
5 Drax Power Station, Yorkshire
6 Tin and Copper
7 Geri Halliwell
8 Miami
9 *Spice*
10 The Keystone State
11 Joe Lieberman
12 Chingford and Woodford Green
13 Iggy Pop
14 The Sage of Omaha
15 Colombia
16 Louis XIII
17 Short Message Service
18 Florian Cloud de Bounevialle O'Malley Armstrong
19 The Cambrian Era
20 The Hollywood Raj

PG. 54

Curious Questions 6

1 Winnie the Pooh
2 Bologna
3 Spetsnaz
4 Harry Nilsson's
5 Mauritius
6 A Herd
7 Longannet
8 Jane Wyman
9 Bolton
10 Gizzard stones
11 More than 2 years
12 13
13 Norman Schwarzkopf
14 *The Pilgrim's Progress*
15 Connie Francis
16 Greece
17 1950
18 Mariana Trench
19 Magnetic Resonance Imaging
20 Rod Serling

PG. 55

Curious Questions 7

1 Chester Racecourse
2 A U (hey you)
3 Military Police
4 Trevor Horn
5 Lyman
6 Oncology
7 He fell down a lift shaft
8 Gateshead Millennium Bridge
9 Amazon
10 Sri Lanka
11 Bolton
12 Melinda
13 Colour Blindness
14 My Little Pony and friends
15 The Trotters
16 3
17 1984
18 Lester Maddox
19 Penny
20 Bengals

PG. 56

Answers

Curious Questions 8

1 Gone But Not Forgotten
2 1948
3 Hippocrates
4 Not Suitable For Work
5 1971
6 Walter Mondale
7 Quincy Jones
8 Beslan
9 5
10 August 15th
11 Valance
12 *Top Cat*
13 1963
14 Ermine Street
15 Unidentified Flying Object
16 8
17 Frank Marshall Davis
18 Florence
19 The Yorkshire Ripper
20 Shaggy (Scooby Doo)

PG. 57

Curious Questions 9

1 Old Faithful
2 Michael Jackson's
3 Cheryl
4 *The Wicker Man*
5 Zulu
6 Simon Le Bon
7 Nathuram Godse
8 Van Diemen's Land
9 Christian Horner
10 Guernsey
11 Muhammad Ali
12 Sir Ian McKellen
13 Liverpool
14 Hamelin
15 Cassius Clay
16 Maurice White
17 The Unification Church
18 Atlanta
19 Evel Knievel
20 1958 FA Cup

PG. 58

Curious Questions 10

1 Billie Piper
2 Fat
3 Garden of Gethsemane
4 *The Tracey Ullman Show*
5 The AD79 Eruption of Vesuvius
6 Near Death Experience
7 Tallahassee
8 Cartmel
9 Elizabeth Taylor
10 Tom Jones
11 Russia
12 Spherical
13 Alexander the Great
14 Cincinnati
15 River Great Ouse
16 Tom Hardy
17 John Lennon Airport
18 The Archies with *Sugar, Sugar*
19 Derek Acorah
20 Sonny Liston

PG. 59

Answers

Curious Questions 11

1 Type of cheese	11 Potato
2 Helen of Troy	12 Every 10 years
3 The Muses	13 Pandemonium
4 Iceland	14 Eric Roberts
5 Fisherman's Friend	15 Engelbert Humperdinck
6 Mel C	16 Barry Goldwater
7 Christie's	17 1993
8 Anchorage	18 Katie Price
9 Manchester United	19 Inspector Gadget
10 Florence, Italy	20 2001

PG. 60

Curious Questions 12

1 Noel and Liam Gallagher	11 Tracey Neville
2 Dermot Desmond	12 British Broadcasting Corporation
3 Chandelier	13 Bishop's Lynn
4 5	14 Canary in the Coal Mine
5 Iain Duncan Smith	15 Florence Nightingale
6 Diane Cilento	16 78
7 Balalaika	17 Greenbelt Festival
8 Hell's Kitchen	18 1976
9 Bishop Auckland	19 Took her for a drink'
10 Israel	20 Keystone

PG. 61

Curious Questions 13

1 Mel Gibson	11 Herge
2 An American roulette wheel has a double zero	12 Mike Gambit
3 David Lynch	13 Wes Craven
4 Blaise Pascal	14 The Rose Bowl Game
5 Brian Robson Rankin	15 Crocodiles
6 Warren Mitchell	16 Hank Marvin
7 Norwich	17 Patrick Stewart
8 Don Henley	18 Fungi
9 John Torode	19 Iain Duncan Smith
10 Nobel Peace Prize	20 Boughton House

PG. 62

Answers

Curious Questions 14

1	36	11	'Oh God'
2	New Haven, Connecticut	12	Max Miller
3	The Shenandoah	13	Doctor Mirabilis
4	Yellowstone	14	Eyes
5	*Spongebob Squarepants*	15	Famous American Newsreader
6	*Ging Gang Goolie*	16	German Measles
7	'Be British'	17	Zero
8	Martin Landau	18	Whistleblower
9	2006	19	1901
10	Bud and Lou	20	Stephen Fry

PG. 63

Curious Questions15

1	*Swan Lake*	11	Herefordshire
2	Rupert Brooke	12	Hello Kitty
3	Patrick John McEnroe	13	The Monica Lewinsky Scandal
4	Burlesque	14	Aramaic
5	Crufts	15	Mr. Bean
6	Second Battle of Ypres	16	Grand Old Party
7	William Howard Taft	17	Clive Woodward
8	Prague	18	*Who's the Boss?*
9	12	19	*Dancing with the stars*
10	The Sweet	20	The Palace of Versailles

PG. 64

Curious Questions 16

1	Santander	11	Betamax
2	The Cenotaph	12	4.30am
3	Kitten	13	St Davids
4	Michael Barratt	14	Neville Neville
5	Stroller	15	Five Beers please
6	US Ambassador to the UK	16	Pink Floyd
7	Ante Meridan	17	Kerry Katona
8	Gateshead	18	Google
9	*Avatar*	19	Parker and Barrow
10	Escapology stunts	20	San Diego

PG. 65

Answers

Curious Questions 17

1. Marti Pellow
2. FALSE
3. The Winklevoss Twins
4. Phil Redmond
5. El Salvador
6. Liverpool
7. Russ Abbott
8. Max Zorin
9. James Brown
10. Angela Lansbury
11. Dwight D Eisenhower
12. Al Jolson
13. John McEnroe
14. Rockatansky
15. HG Wells
16. Sharon
17. The Cultural Revolution
18. *Silent Spring*
19. Americans by far
20. Michael Phelps

PG. 66

Curious Questions 18

1. 10.50%
2. Mondelēz International
3. Dennis Potter
4. Architecture
5. Billy Joel
6. *Dora the Explorer*
7. Stephen Fry
8. Quincy Jones
9. Rob Ford
10. Brian Connolly
11. Hilary Devey
12. The Perrier Award
13. 1964
14. Greatest Living Yorkshireman
15. 1967
16. Rachel Carson
17. Sarah Brightman
18. Comic Books
19. Cow
20. Harry Gordon Selfridge

PG. 67

England and Wales 1

1. Hampshire
2. Beer
3. The Lake District
4. Kent
5. Frimley Green
6. Liverpool
7. Aberfan
8. Welwyn Garden City
9. The Fens
10. Swansea
11. Red
12. Kent
13. Middlesbrough
14. Consett
15. River Towy
16. Westminster School
17. Tredegar
18. Clumber Park, Nottingham
19. Magdalen Tower
20. Shropshire

PG. 68

Answers

England and Wales 2

1. Stowe
2. Cuddle
3. Pitmatic
4. Stamford
5. Anglesey
6. Manchester
7. East Anglia
8. Nottingham
9. Denbighshire
10. Scunthorpe
11. Chadderton
12. Liverpool
13. South Yorkshire is landlocked
14. Sheffield
15. Golden Cap
16. River Sheaf
17. Ribblehead Viaduct
18. Doncaster
19. Prestatyn
20. Loughborough

PG. 69

England and Wales 3

1. Scholes
2. Polperro
3. Brighton
4. East Sussex
5. Guildford Cathedral
6. Yorkshire
7. Winchester
8. Lindisfarne
9. Wycombe
10. Hounslow
11. Mushy peas
12. Ron Flowers
13. Whitby
14. River Wharfe
15. Anglesey
16. The Battle of Flamborough Head
17. The Blackpool Illuminations
18. Spurn Point
19. Holyhead
20. Pembrokeshire

PG. 70

England and Wales 4

1. London
2. Boston
3. Warrington
4. Gethin Jones
5. St John's Wood
6. Porthleven
7. Leeds
8. Royal Berkshire
9. Birmingham
10. It has a crooked/ twisted spire
11. Hampshire
12. RAF Fylingdales
13. Godalming
14. Pontypridd
15. Rotherham
16. Hertfordshire
17. Middlesbrough
18. Wensleydale
19. Isle of Wight
20. Tiger Bay

PG. 71

Answers

Family Ties

1	Konnie Huq	11	David Tennant
2	Cleo Laine	12	Nicole Richie
3	Jo Johnson	13	Helen Hunt
4	O.J. Simpson	14	Russell Brand
5	Keith Chegwin	15	Johnathan Ross
6	Neil Gaiman	16	Rocco
7	Elton John	17	Baldwin
8	Sacha Baron Cohen	18	11
9	Barry Van Dyke	19	Jay-Z
10	Crystal Gayle	20	Giles Coren

PG. 72

Famous Barrys

1	Barry Sotero	11	Barry Dennis
2	Barry Davies	12	Barry Venison
3	Barry Sheene	13	Barry Chuckle
4	Shaun Williamson	14	Barry Foster
5	Barry Bostwick	15	Barry Island, Wales
6	Barry Cryer	16	Barry Gibb
7	Barry Manilow	17	Barry Ferguson
8	Barry McGuigan	18	Barry Humphries
9	Barry Scott	19	Barry John
10	Barry Goldwater	20	Barry White

PG. 73

Films 1

1	Clint Eastwood	11	*The Life of Brian*
2	Colin Welland	12	7
3	*The Wrath of Khan*	13	*The Grand Budapest Hotel*
4	*The Silence of the Lambs*	14	*The Third Man*
5	Martin Scorcese	15	*Zulu*
6	*Gone with the wind*	16	8
7	Danny Dyer	17	7
8	*Fatal Attraction*	18	Robert de Niro
9	Brian De Palma	19	*Amity*
10	Wes Anderson	20	*Braveheart*

PG. 74

Answers

Films 2

1　George Lazenby
2　Frank Abignale
3　Cary Grant
4　*Men in Black*
5　*The Others*
6　Jessica Chastain
7　1960s
8　*Superman*
9　Tom Cruise
10　*On the Rocks*

11　No - that year it was won by
　　Shakespeare in Love
12　*Sideways*
13　Bert
14　Ron Howard
15　Edgar Allan Poe
16　Mel Gibson
17　*Jigsaw*
18　Michael Caine OR ALEC GUINNESS
19　1985
20　Terrence Malick

PG. 75

Films 3

1　Steve Reeves
2　Jeremy Irons
3　The Sharks and The Jets
4　*Peggy Sue Got Married*
5　*Gandhi*
6　Samuel L. Jackson
7　An Orange
8　Billy Zane
9　*Stop! Or My Mom Will Shoot*
10　*It Happened One Night*

11　Jodie Foster
12　American
13　Roseanne Barr
14　*Harry Potter and the Deathly
　　Hallows – Part 2*
15　The Italian Stallion
16　Frank Borzage
17　Harold Lloyd
18　*The Silver Linings Playbook*
19　John Carpenter
20　*Runaway Bride*

PG. 76

Films 4

1　*The Bodyguard*
2　Bruce Beresford
3　Chevy Chase
4　Michelle Rodriguez
5　The Emerald City
6　Timothy Spall
7　Chuck Norris
8　*Donnie Darko*
9　*Cutthroat Island*
10　Robert Carlyle

11　*Monster's University*
12　Willem Dafoe
13　*Argo*
14　Linda Gray's
15　Martin Scorcese
16　*Manhunter*
17　*Dick Tracy*
18　*Reservoir Dogs*
19　Sarah Connor
20　Peter Cattaneo

PG. 77

Answers

Films 5

1	1993	11	Tim Burton
2	Noel Coward	12	Brigitte Nielsen
3	*The Revenant*	13	*Wild*
4	*The Hills Have Eyes*	14	*The Godfather*
5	*Child's Play*	15	*The Wolf of Wall Street*
6	Stanley Kubrick	16	Christina Ricci
7	*Saw*	17	*Moneyball*
8	No Black Directors have won an Oscar	18	Carl Orff
9	Rock Hudson	19	Ang Lee
10	*Home Alone*	20	Overlook Hotel

PG. 78

Food & Drink 1

1	Gastronomy	11	Borscht
2	Kiwi	12	Steak
3	Chocolate	13	Wispa
4	Bubble tea	14	A Sandwich
5	Marmite	15	Reggae Reggae
6	Gumbo	16	Vegan+E12
7	Goulash	17	Coffee
8	Kedgeree	18	Shirley Temple
9	Loganberry	19	Hazelnut
10	1930	20	Sesame

PG. 79

Food & Drink 2

1	Pho	11	Curry
2	Semolina	12	Paella
3	Dairy product	13	Durum Wheat
4	Cayenne Pepper	14	Clementine
5	Double Decker	15	Norwich
6	Laverbread	16	Avocado
7	Mulligatawny	17	Halloumi
8	Pizza	18	Cola
9	Cheese and Onion	19	Choux
10	Sausage	20	Round flat quick bread

PG. 80

Answers

Football

1	Tranmere Rovers	11	Anfield
2	Dublin	12	Hibernian
3	Cameroon	13	Roy Carroll
4	Nagoya Grampus Eight	14	Taylor Report
5	Craig Brown	15	Norman Whiteside
6	Bournemouth	16	Jim Leighton
7	Pat Jennings	17	Atletico Madrid
8	Bramall Lane	18	West Germany
9	Charlie Nicholas	19	St Andrew's
10	Watford	20	William

PG. 81

General Knowledge 1

1	Anne Robinson	11	President James Monroe
2	*The Beano*	12	Richard Osman
3	*The Dandy*	13	Canadian
4	A tightrope walker	14	Halfords
5	A Condominium	15	Jeremy Paxman
6	April (30th)	16	Bavarian Motor Works
7	*Pied-à-terre*	17	*Extras*
8	*Top of the Form*	18	Fish and Chips
9	Wrestling (a WWE tag team)	19	Swampy
10	Medium-density fibreboard	20	Red

PG. 82

General Knowledge 2

1	*After Dark*	11	Mafia
2	Fort William	12	Thirteen
3	*Punch*	13	Dreyfuss
4	Neil Hamilton	14	Steve Martin and John Candy
5	Ealing	15	1994
6	Atlantic	16	1500 metres
7	St Louis	17	*War of the Roses*
8	Belize	18	Norma Jeane Mortenson
9	Israel, Jordan	19	Ronnie Wood
10	Bruce Willis	20	Ken Dodd

PG. 83

Answers

General Knowledge 3

1 The Pretenders
2 Bros
3 New Order
4 Bananaman
5 Billy Bunter
6 Maureen Rees
7 Eton
8 Mercury
9 Hippopotamus
10 Trees
11 Cyprus
12 Tim Brooke-Taylor
13 Iraq
14 Percy Thrower
15 Boris Karloff
16 Jon Pertwee
17 *South Park*
18 *Muppet Show*
19 Judith Durham
20 Irving Berlin

PG. 84

General Knowledge 4

1 Rio Ferdinand
2 Jean Harlow
3 Denmark
4 Zambia
5 Queensland
6 Matalan
7 18 hours
8 Tonka
9 Ann Summers
10 400m hurdles
11 West Ham Utd.
12 Chicago Blackhawks
13 Sonny Liston
14 John McEnroe
15 Georgie Fame
16 *Denis*
17 Brian Epstein
18 Thomas More
19 Sean Bean
20 One

PG. 85

General Knowledge 5

1 Six
2 Uranus
3 Manchester
4 Wine
5 Spirals
6 Michael Foot
7 *Our House*
8 Matt Dawson
9 October 21st
10 May 4th
11 1980s
12 The 1940s
13 The 1980s
14 The Bessemer Process
15 A Cow
16 He called for his pipe, and he called for his bowl and he called for his fiddlers three
17 Germany
18 Fox
19 German (and French and Dutch)
20 Union

PG. 86

Answers

General Knowledge 6

1 Land of Fire
2 Deer
3 Hugo 'Hurley' Reyes
4 John Candy
5 Paul Scholes (by over 100 games)
6 3
7 121
8 180
9 Orange
10 2004
11 Kid Jensen
12 *Baa Baa Black Sheep*
13 The Moon
14 The Blind Beggar
15 Talksport
16 Borsetshire
17 Victoria Derbyshire
18 1990
19 *The Shipping Forecast*
20 Chris Moyles

PG. 87

General Knowledge 7

1 Feedback
2 1215
3 Douglas Adams
4 Kenneth Williams
5 Clare Balding
6 Shock Jock
7 Zoo
8 Nicholas Parsons
9 Steve Wright
10 Shylock
11 Athens
12 *Romeo and Juliet*
13 Cerveza
14 Ich liebe dich
15 Japanese
16 Spanish
17 Reich
18 Richard Bachman
19 Cujo
20 Pepper Potts

PG. 88

General Knowledge 8

1 Ross McWhirter
2 Arsenal
3 Tunisia
4 Samuel Johnson
5 Herbert Hoover
6 Smoke and Fog
7 Hello
8 Tony
9 Sunderland
10 Almond
11 *The Police*
12 Elizabeth Tower
13 Alaska
14 Danish
15 Howard Hughes
16 Southern Cross
17 Mackeson
18 1981
19 Pussy Riot
20 Anton Drexler

PG. 89

Answers

General Knowledge 9

1 Lentils
2 *Rumpole of the Bailey*
3 Surfing
4 Ceefax
5 Duke of York
6 *Oracle*
7 Hull
8 Felt tip pen
9 Memphis
10 Chromium
11 Margaret Thatcher Day
12 *The Artist*
13 Julian Clary
14 Margaret Thatcher
15 Carol and Mark
16 *Gangnam Style*
17 Ash
18 Kenneth Branagh
19 Francois
20 Mitt Romney

PG. 90

General Knowledge 10

1 Leveson
2 Mars
3 Gloriana
4 Dave Brubeck
5 Adele
6 Queen Anne
7 Washington Monument
8 The Gherkin
9 Taj Mahal
10 Jupiter
11 Her face
12 Miracles
13 Free school milk
14 Jeremy Thorpe
15 Premium Bonds
16 ERNIE
17 1980s
18 Chickpeas
19 Greece
20 Gazpacho

PG. 91

General Knowledge 11

1 Napoleon
2 Stefan Edberg
3 Ravens
4 Witness
5 Beagle
6 Pigs
7 Elliott
8 Renee and Renato
9 The Firm
10 Piccadilly
11 As a choreographer
12 Shanghai
13 Twentieth
14 Methane
15 Orville Wright
16 Walker Brothers
17 Tudor
18 Canada
19 Manchester, Edinburgh, Cardiff
20 Italy

PG. 92

Answers

General Knowledge 12

1	Aidensfield	11	Bradley Walsh
2	Rooster	12	Rob Brydon
3	Dounreay	13	Chris Evert
4	Fast Breeder Reactor	14	Sioux
5	Suzi Quatro	15	Seasonal Affective Disorder
6	Winona Ryder	16	Chucky
7	Brown, Princeton, Columbia, Cornell	17	New York
8	Gillette	18	Foreigners
9	Nat King Cole	19	Formic
10	Costa Concordia	20	Michael Moore

PG. 93

General Knowledge 13

1	Delaware	11	Basil
2	British Honduras	12	Italian cream cheese
3	*Goldenballs*	13	Chubby Brown
4	Pumas	14	Stanley Kubrick
5	*Jingle All The Way*	15	Red
6	Danny Kaye	16	Tank
7	James	17	Geoffrey Palmer
8	Battenberg	18	*Going Straight*
9	Fish heads	19	Ben Elton
10	Walnuts	20	Karen Gillan

PG. 94

General Knowledge 14

1	Brooke Shields	11	Foggy
2	Greg Lake	12	Perfume
3	Steve Martin	13	Kyoto
4	Billy Crystal	14	Shangri-La
5	*Air Force One*	15	*The Borrowers*
6	Pole vault	16	*Just William*
7	Ruud Gullit	17	Alaska
8	Mike Hailwood	18	Tomsk
9	Cathy Gale	19	Zambezi
10	Mr Freeze	20	THRUSH

PG. 95

Answers

General Knowledge 15

1	Clarice Starling	11	Birch
2	*Budgie*	12	Muriel Spark
3	1990	13	*Coronation Street*
4	Zaire	14	Castanets
5	John McCarthy	15	Tchaichovsky
6	P .T.Barnum	16	7
7	Van Gogh	17	Juventus
8	Marco Polo	18	Jennifer Saunders
9	Gomez	19	Proctor & Gamble
10	*Macbeth*	20	*Nine*

PG. 96

General Knowledge 16

1	*Dukes of Hazzard*	11	Seven
2	Ken	12	Faberge
3	Edward Heath	13	Dean Martin
4	Blue	14	Dave Allen
5	White	15	Darling
6	Japan	16	*Charlie & The Chocolate Factory*
7	Cain	17	300
8	St Leger	18	Local Defence Volunteers
9	*Downton Abbey*	19	Titanic
10	Charles De Gaulle	20	Three

PG. 97

General Knowledge 17

1	L'Oreal	11	Snooker
2	*T J Hooker*	12	University Boat race
3	*Silent Witness*	13	Show Jumping
4	Acid	14	Brazilian
5	2016	15	Quiz Shows (especially *Jeopardy* in the US)
6	Boston Strangler	16	Garibaldi
7	Deep Purple	17	Stayed at home
8	*Albatross*	18	Richard Nixon
9	Elton John	19	Idi Amin
10	Paul Weller	20	Sir Walter Raleigh

PG. 98

Answers

General Knowledge 18

1	Pat Phoenix	11	Roast Beef
2	Hats	12	Tin
3	Jessica	13	Golf
4	Dame Edna Everidge	14	*Ivor the Engine*
5	Charles Dickens	15	Flute
6	Wet Wet Wet	16	Lungs
7	Damon Hill	17	Eyes
8	L'Escargot	18	Benny Goodman
9	Bjorn Borg	19	The treatment of Native Americans
10	Carla Lane	20	Swansea & Neath

PG. 99

General Knowledge 19

1	D. H. Lawrence	11	Kelvin MacKenzie
2	Doomsday Book	12	*Today*
3	Peter Lilley	13	Rachel Beer (in 1891)
4	St Moritz	14	E-mail
5	Stamen	15	Trevor Baylis
6	Torbay	16	George Washington Carver
7	Andy Warhol	17	John Logie Baird
8	Sinking of the Titanic	18	Caresse Crosby
9	Japan	19	The Flushing Toilet
10	Due to its coverage of the Hillsborough Disaster	20	The Electric Guitar

PG. 100

Geography 1

1	France	11	What is now Morocco, Algeria, Tunisia, and Libya
2	Baffin Island	12	Lausanne
3	Isohyet	13	Scotland, England, Northern Ireland and Wales
4	7925 miles (approx.)	14	China
5	Canada	15	Canada
6	Split	16	Mafadi
7	Mediterranean	17	Murmansk
8	Calypso Deep	18	Oman
9	Egypt	19	Strait of Hormuz
10	Switzerland	20	The Orinoco

PG. 101

Answers

Geography 2

1	The Low Countries	11	Germany
2	Spain	12	The Netherlands
3	Mont Blanc	13	Doha
4	Nauru	14	Brazil
5	Denmark	15	Suriname
6	Galicia	16	Cape Horn
7	Cern	17	Longitude
8	Cantons	18	The Gambia
9	Nepal and China	19	Patagonia
10	Mexico	20	Chile

PG. 102

History 1

1	They dressed as Native Americans	11	Granada
2	Rhacotis	12	Saladin
3	Cameronians	13	Executed by Firing Squad
4	East India Company	14	1707
5	Dr Thomas Arnold	15	A cell attached to a church
6	The Byzantine Empire	16	1215
7	Downham Market	17	Dr Beeching
8	Pharaoh	18	Churches
9	First Opium War	19	Lighthouses
10	Hampton Court Palace	20	Leicester

PG. 103

History 2

1	Latin	11	China
2	Anne of Denmark	12	9 days
3	Endeavour	13	Francisco
4	Falkirk	14	1897
5	1961	15	Lambert Simnel
6	Lech Walesa	16	Henry VII
7	Poland	17	1953
8	Scotland	18	Leonid Brezhnev
9	Andy Gilchrist	19	Voting
10	The Gunpowder Plot	20	William Penn

PG. 104

Answers

History 3

1	Plantagenet	11	James Watt
2	Francis II of France	12	The Industrial Revolution
3	Pope Alexander VI	13	Austria and Germany
4	Venice	14	Prussia
5	Horatia	15	Czechoslovakia
6	Flapper	16	Hibernia
7	1968	17	The Rubicon
8	1928	18	Grigori
9	1929	19	Queen Victoria
10	2000	20	Edward Smith

PG. 105

History 4

1	Chartwell	11	Jimmy Carter
2	Monhadas	12	A UFO
3	Gavrilo Princip	13	Malia and Sasha
4	Los Angeles	14	James Garfield
5	Muammar Gaddafi	15	Andrew Johnson
6	White	16	Finland and The Soviet Union
7	James Young Simpson	17	1953
8	Ermine Street	18	1931
9	Ulysses S. Grant	19	1949
10	Lyndon B Johnson	20	1963

PG. 106

Horse racing

1	The Dubai World Cup	11	Ruby
2	Meydan	12	Walter Swinburn
3	Epsom	13	Willie Carson
4	She was the first woman jockey to win The Melbourne Cup	14	Sha Tin
5	Secretariat	15	Tony McCoy
6	26 times	16	Coolmore
7	It was extended to 4 days	17	Godolphin
8	8	18	The Jockey Club
9	59	19	Newmarket
10	The Chair	20	The Grand National

PG. 107

Answers

How Many?

1 640	11 8
2 196 (if you count Taiwan)	12 20
3 366	13 5
4 5	14 3
5 8	15 12
6 52	16 15 weeks
7 1 (for *True Grit*)	17 40
8 285 miles	18 9
9 0	19 66
10 4	20 7

PG. 108

In the News

1 Hugo Chavez	11 The recreational use of laughing gas
2 Jeffrey Epstein	12 Tom Watson
3 Nigel Farage	13 Shaker Aamer
4 Leanne Wood	14 Grant Shapps
5 Helen Macdonald	15 The Jungle
6 Jihadi John	16 The Cenotaph
7 Kim Sears	17 Apple
8 56	18 The Eagles of Death Metal
9 65,000,000	19 Hans Blix
10 Crash for Cash	20 Chelsea physio

PG. 109

In What Year?

1 1896	11 1970
2 2002	12 2007
3 1981	13 1995
4 1940	14 1990
5 1992	15 1991
6 1997	16 1314
7 2012	17 1946
8 1982	18 1979
9 2011	19 1989
10 2011	20 1985

PG. 110

Answers

Inventions

1 Nikola Tesla
2 Zumba
3 A Guillotine
4 Jacques Costeau
5 The TV remote control
6 White out (Tipp-Ex)
7 Adrian Frutiger
8 Catherine De Medici
9 Jeans
10 John Napier
11 Minecraft
12 Nutella
13 Frank Zamboni
14 The Steadicam
15 Phillips Screwdriver
16 George Cayley
17 Velcro
18 Barnes Wallace
19 Wernher von Braun
20 Jacuzzi

PG. 111

Ireland

1 Waterford
2 County Cork
3 Waterford
4 Jack Charlton
5 Galway
6 Giant's Causeway
7 Ballymena
8 1690
9 Clontarf
10 Brian Boru
11 Leinster
12 The Pale
13 County Kildare
14 River Liffey
15 County Kerry
16 Queen's University
17 Place of
18 George Best
19 County Tyrone
20 Derry

PG. 112

Italy

1 Cagliari
2 Papa
3 Bologna
4 Savoy
5 1512
6 1871
7 The Eternal City
8 Waldensians
9 6
10 Milan
11 Silvio Berlusconi
12 Perugia
13 Wolf
14 San Marino and The Vatican City
15 Volcanoes
16 Rossi
17 St Mark
18 Naples
19 *Scudo*
20 Leonardo Da Vinci

PG. 113

Answers

Jobs

1	Barber	11	Ombudsman
2	Electrician	12	Screenwriter
3	Waiter/ Waitress	13	Publicist
4	Fire Fighter	14	Choreographer
5	Dentist	15	Stenographer
6	Drayman	16	Ghillie
7	Butler	17	Croupier
8	Cooper	18	Sommelier
9	Podiatrist	19	Costermonger
10	Projectionist	20	Medium

PG. 114

Let's Get Quizzy! 1

1	Penfold	11	Teavee
2	Rubble	12	Plantation of Ulster
3	Cruella De Vil	13	St Bees
4	Blue	14	Lutine
5	John Fashanu	15	*Broadchurch*
6	Duchy of Lancaster	16	Mayor of New York
7	Dvorak keyboards	17	Dubrovnik
8	22	18	Sue Perkins
9	Blackmail	19	*The Huffington Post*
10	Salieri	20	Wetherspoons

PG. 115

Let's Get Quizzy! 2

1	S4C	11	Bournemouth
2	Watling Street	12	Area 51
3	Nike	13	Norway
4	Carmel	14	Penny Red
5	Cairo	15	Blue Zones
6	Hershey	16	Norman Bates
7	Gerhard Schroder	17	David Koresh
8	ITN	18	November
9	Caitlyn Jenner	19	Champ
10	Swim the Channel	20	7 - 1990 to 1997

PG. 116

Answers

Let's Get Quizzy! 3

1	Janette Tough	11	Wima
2	Joint Photographic Experts Group	12	Winston Churchill
3	Jeb	13	Winnie
4	Judi Dench	14	Denis Thatcher
5	Vegetable	15	Esther Rantzen
6	Wallpaper	16	Diurnal
7	Dog Whistle	17	Cairns
8	The New Deal	18	Julia Carling
9	Bubbles	19	Ramsay MacDonald
10	Elevation	20	Wagga Wagga

PG. 117

Let's Get Quizzy! 4

1	Jazz	11	Ruud Gullitt
2	Père Lachaise Cemetery	12	Wine
3	Mashed Potato	13	Simon Cadell
4	Mike Myers	14	Abraham Lincoln said it to Harriet Beecher Stowe
5	Earache	15	New Zealand
6	Punctuality	16	Fuchsia
7	Only Connect	17	Defence Secretary
8	Georgia	18	The Sundance Film Festival
9	Fargo	19	Dutch
10	Randy Newman	20	1000 kg

PG. 118

Let's Get Quizzy! 5

1	Frederick Forsyth	11	Flute
2	Green	12	Charles Perrault
3	Oprah Winfrey	13	Audrey
4	Sir Edwin Lutyens	14	Theatres
5	Alnwick Castle	15	Emma Noble
6	Prenton Park	16	Michael Kitchen
7	Steven Spielberg	17	Gordon Strachan
8	Lima	18	Melanie and Martina
9	Sandbanks	19	A sword
10	Barbara Bach	20	Esperanto

PG. 119

Answers

Let's Get Quizzy! 6

1   Greenland
2   Sao Paulo
3   Patagonia
4   San Francisco
5   Real Ale
6   17:00
7   Clara Bow
8   *The Full Monty*
9   Topiary
10 Napoleon III
11 Charles Atlas
12 Glamis Castle
13 Louise Mensch
14 Grimsby
15 Percy Shaw
16 Michelle Keegan
17 LinkedIn
18 The Samaritans
19 Kim Wilde
20 FW de Klerk

PG. 120

Let's Get Quizzy! 7

1   Nostradamus
2   United Parcel Service
3   Ireland
4   Shanghai
5   Milk of water buffalos
6   Offa's Dyke
7   Fermentation
8   Suffolk
9   Ludo
10 Now who would live in a house like this'
11 *Chitty, Chitty, Bang, Bang*
12 Mother Theresa
13 Blue Zones
14 University of Glasgow
15 Osama bin Laden
16 Hussein
17 Camel and a Leopard
18 Goldfinger
19 Simon Rimmer
20 Socks with gaps for your toes

PG. 121

Let's Get Quizzy! 8

1   Scotland
2   Bedrock
3   Dubrovnik
4   Jules Rimet Trophy
5   Batter
6   KLM
7   Peter Dickson
8   *Ludo*
9   Tesco
10 751
11 Wales
12 Mah Jong
13 Camilla Dallerup
14 Nigel Havers
15 Andy Flintoff
16 Joseph of Arimathea
17 Charles Bridge
18 Energy
19 Noel Edmonds
20 Paul Simon

PG. 122

Answers

Let's Get Quizzy! 9

1 Donald Trump
2 Pottery
3 Veritas
4 Vancouver
5 Rome
6 *3rd rock from the Sun*
7 Cat food
8 Tatler
9 Clowns
10 Our Graham
11 Chocolate
12 Harry Houdini
13 White Red Yellow Orange Blue Green
14 Matthew Modine
15 Hawaii
16 Pain threshold
17 Ayman al-Zawahiri
18 E
19 Thomas Jefferson
20 Hovercraft

PG. 123

Let's Get Quizzy! 10

1 Sao Paolo
2 Seventeenth (1636)
3 13
4 7
5 37 pence
6 Belt
7 Showaddywaddy
8 10%
9 Monaco
10 Pink
11 *The Eggheads*
12 Birkenhead
13 *Bellboy*
14 *Don't Know Much*
15 John Smith
16 Foxes
17 St Bees
18 Viscount
19 Widow Twankey
20 The BeeGees

PG. 124

Let's Get Quizzy! 11

1 Shirley Temple
2 Parachute Regiment
3 Plane Crash
4 Tunnocks
5 Coma
6 Puffins
7 1950s
8 Bear Grylls
9 A Nautical Mile
10 Flintshire
11 Oregon
12 David Lynch
13 Rolling Stock
14 Charlotte Church
15 Italy
16 *Peter Pan*
17 Suggs
18 George II
19 Agrippina
20 Three roads

PG. 125

Answers

Let's Get Quizzy! 12

1 Atlas
2 Captain Webb
3 Steven Spielberg
4 Michael Aspel
5 The Stoop
6 P
7 Arthur
8 Irvine Welsh
9 Premium Bonds
10 Elias
11 Toontown
12 Chester
13 Darren Gough
14 Waterloo
15 Boxing Day
16 Cornwall
17 Butchers – hence his nickname
18 Grasses
19 Gabbana (of Dolce and Gabbana fame)
20 Japan

PG. 126

Let's Get Quizzy! 13

1 Harlequins
2 A Burning Bush
3 Lincoln Cathedral
4 Odd Job
5 German
6 Court Jester
7 Rhubarb
8 Richard Branson
9 Greenland
10 Jim Carter
11 WHSmith
12 David Shayler
13 Great Dane
14 Wales
15 Gavin Henson
16 Bond Street
17 3
18 Flemish bond
19 Cricket
20 1937

PG. 127

Let's Get Quizzy! 14

1 Padstow
2 Suggs
3 Laura Ingalls Wilder
4 Oxford
5 Robert Kilroy-Silk
6 Chillingham
7 Apollo 13
8 Dodi Fayed
9 Stavros Flatley
10 High Street
11 Kate Thornton
12 Galileo
13 1982
14 Milli Vanilli
15 Cheltenham Racecourse
16 *Harry Potter*
17 Cambridge (Massachusetts)
18 Connecticut
19 Principal Boy
20 False – it's a passageway for large crowds to exit a theatre or stadium

PG. 128

Answers

Let's Get Quizzy! 15

1   Frank Farian
2   Morag
3   Trivia facts
4   1500
5   Lincoln
6   Ullage
7   Hunter S. Thompson
8   F. Murray Abraham
9   Bread
10 Michelle
11 Sherwood Forest
12 Argentinian
13 Belgian
14 Garden of Gethsemane
15 Ashley Banjo
16 John Profumo
17 *Stella*
18 London Stansted Airport
19 Orville the Duck
20 Nuclear Power Stations

PG. 129

Let's Get Quizzy! 16

1   Whitewash
2   Violet
3   Five
4   Edward
5   Chelsea
6   Speedway
7   Necker Island
8   Decathlon
9   California Highway Patrol
10 Michael Flatley
11 12
12 Denbighshire
13 David Frost
14 Moscow
15 1990
16 Heather Small
17 Queen of the South
18 Gravity
19 Charles Dickens
20 The Humber Bridge

PG. 130

Let's Get Quizzy! 17

1   Richard Nixon
2   *The Taming of the Shrew*
3   Pain
4   Cohort
5   *Sale of the Century*
6   Kendo
7   Hollandaise
8   Muswell Hill
9   85
10 2010
11 *Jack and the Beanstalk*
12 *Outnumbered*
13 Christopher Cockerell
14 Maidstone
15 Dacia
16 Mars
17 The Taliban
18 A tidal phenomenon in which the leading edge of the incoming tide forms a wave
19 *Game of Thrones*
20 All held the post of New York City mayor

PG. 131

Answers

Let's Get Quizzy! 18

1	Do It Yourself	11	Michael Williams
2	Wile E. Coyote	12	Clementine
3	*I am the Walrus*	13	Mr Potato Head
4	Pat Sharp	14	Babylon
5	Pine nuts	15	Supermarine
6	Thursday	16	Alfred Hitchcock
7	Newfoundland	17	Albert Dock, Liverpool
8	Alan Shepard	18	Crossbow
9	Stratford Upon Avon	19	Nevada
10	Death Penalty	20	Leicester Tigers

PG. 132

Let's Get Quizzy! 19

1	Walmart	11	10 – 4
2	Bob Holness	12	Alamo
3	Witney	13	Skegness
4	Indonesia	14	Go West
5	Norma	15	Toxic shock syndrome
6	London	16	Melbourne
7	Drew Barrymore	17	No frills
8	Haddock	18	Uruguay
9	The French Riveria	19	3
10	Ghetto	20	Erin Boag

PG. 133

London

1	Euston Road	11	Zoological Society of London
2	'Boris Bikes'	12	Staples Corner
3	Parliament Square	13	Surrey
4	Lambeth Palace	14	Silicon Roundabout
5	Teddington	15	Café Royal
6	Eel Pie Island	16	St Pauls Cathedral
7	King Charles I	17	Shepherd's Bush
8	Whitehall	18	St. Paul's Cathedral
9	Wapping	19	Pimlico
10	Woolwich	20	'The Walkie-Talkie'

PG. 134

Answers

Music 1

1. *Black or White*
2. *One Day in Your Life*
3. Neverland
4. Twice
5. *This Is It*
6. Los Angeles
7. Prince, Paris and Michael Jnr
8. Exeter City
9. *Moonwalker*
10. Cab Calloway
11. Thriller
12. Vincent Price
13. Pepsi Cola
14. *Spiderman*
15. Don McLean
16. Gary Numan
17. Lynn Anderson
18. Showaddywaddy
19. *Show me the Way*
20. Kate Bush

PG. 135

Music 2

1. Prince
2. Peter Tork
3. *Scream*
4. Malcolm McLaren
5. Smokey Robinson
6. *September*
7. Bill Wyman
8. Ragtime
9. *Ride a White Swan*
10. Rockabilly
11. Bongos
12. Zither
13. Paul Anka
14. Cheryl
15. Notorious B.I.G
16. *The Sting*
17. *D.I.V.O.R.C.E.*
18. Woodwind
19. Tuba
20. Escape

PG. 136

Music 3

1. The Rolling Stones
2. Italy
3. OMD
4. *Video Killed the Radio Star*
5. E
6. Piano
7. Prokofiev
8. Cole Porter
9. *You Really Got Me*
10. Connie Francis
11. *The One and Only*
12. The Temperance Seven
13. Neil Tennant and Chris Lowe
14. Shirley Manson
15. Culture Club
16. Richard and Karen
17. Roger Daltrey
18. Neil Diamond
19. ZZ Top
20. *Enigma Variations*

PG. 137

Answers

Music 4

1	*Variations*	11	Jimmy Nail
2	3	12	Roger Taylor
3	February	13	Simon and Garfunkel
4	Santana	14	Kenny G
5	Jeff Lynne	15	*Perfect Day*
6	Giorgio Moroder	16	*Move on Up*
7	*I want to break free*	17	JLS
8	The Cheeky Girls	18	Natalie Cole
9	Brian May	19	Oingo Boingo
10	Creedence Clearwater Revival	20	*The Minute Waltz*

PG. 138

Musicals

1	*Chess*	11	Larry Hagman
2	*The Rocky Horror Picture Show*	12	Jack Wild
3	*Chess*	13	Cameron Mackintosh
4	*Me and My Girl*	14	Leonard Bernstein
5	*Annie Get Your Gun*	15	*Hair*
6	*Rent*	16	*The Lion King*
7	*Blood Brothers*	17	*The Phantom of the Opera*
8	Richard O' Brien	18	*Oklahoma!*
9	*Chicago*	19	*My Fair Lady*
10	*Sweet Charity*	20	*A Chorus Line*

PG. 139

Myths and Legends

1	Proxenus of Atarneus	11	The monarchy will crumble
2	Helios	12	Ceres
3	Hector	13	Avalon
4	Apollo	14	The Lady of the Lake
5	Nessie	15	Merlin
6	The Green Man	16	Rosslyn Chapel
7	Sherwood Forest	17	The Valkyries
8	*Bigfoot*	18	Asgard
9	Romania	19	Odin (Woden)
10	Bigfoot/ Sasquatch	20	Human and Bull

PG. 140

Answers

Newspapers

1. The Wapping Dispute
2. Richard Desmond
3. Disgusted of Tunbridge Wells'
4. *The Boston Globe*
5. *The Stage*
6. *The Wall Street Journal*
7. *The Observer*
8. *The Manchester Guardian*
9. *The Daily Telegraph*
10. Robert Maxwell
11. *News of the World*
12. *The Mirror*
13. *Irish Independent*
14. *New Day*
15. *Leads*
16. *The Guardian*
17. *Leicester Mercury*
18. *The Sunday Post*
19. *The New York Times*
20. *Daily Express*

PG. 141

Opening Lines

1. (Theme from) *New York New York*
2. *Smoke gets in your eyes*
3. *Just Like Jesse James*
4. It's Christmas time, there's no need to be afraid
5. *Tragedy*
6. *What if God was one of us*
7. *Diana*
8. *The Lion Sleeps Tonight*
9. *The Skye Boat Song*
10. *My heart will go on*
11. *Money Money Money*
12. *Love is all around*
13. *The boys of Summer*
14. 'One, two, three o'clock, four o'clock rock'
15. *Eleanor Rigby*
16. 1999
17. 'If you like to gamble I tell you I'm your man'
18. Jimi Hendrix
19. *Never Tear Us Apart*
20. *Great Balls of Fire*

PG. 142

Politics 1

1. A Radical
2. Right Wing
3. Civil Disobedience
4. Michael Martin
5. John Prescott
6. Grant Shapps
7. Minister Without Portfolio
8. Malcolm Pearson, Baron Pearson of Rannoch
9. George Younger
10. The Division Bell
11. Pegida UK
12. United Kingdom Independence Party
13. Red
14. Keir Hardie
15. Nigel Farage
16. Michael Foot
17. Chesterfield
18. Magdalen College, Oxford
19. Labour isn't working
20. The Fabian Society

PG. 143

Answers

Politics 2

1 David Cameron
2 Ebbw Vale
3 Greenham Common
4 Simon Hughes
5 Tatton
6 Mormon
7 Canada
8 Henry Cabot Lodge
9 Richard Nixon
10 'Just Say No'
11 Mitt Romney
12 The 19th Amendment
13 Dick Cheney
14 Super Tuesday
15 Feel the Bern
16 Every 4 years
17 Bernie Sanders
18 The First Lady
19 They continue to be called "President"
20 International Brotherhood of Teamsters

PG. 144

Pot Luck 1

1 Michael Palin
2 When diving
3 Irish
4 1980s
5 *Are you being served?*
6 4
7 Dan Brown
8 1955
9 Luxembourg
10 Self-contained Underwater Breathing Apparatus
11 Opencast
12 The act of selling church offices and roles
13 Libya
14 Terry Gilliam
15 Nigella
16 Mojito
17 'Yabba Dabba Doo'
18 Quackery
19 Camerlengo
20 John Cena

PG. 145

Pot Luck 2

1 Feet
2 Fanny Craddock
3 60
4 The 1963 Great Train Robbery
5 Scarborough
6 Ottawa
7 Silk
8 Ernest Hemingway
9 Rolf Harris
10 Mozambique
11 Dorothy, Rose, Blanche and Sophia
12 5
13 The Duke of Wellington
14 John
15 Monday's Child
16 Bob Geldof
17 Aluminium
18 £200
19 John Cleese
20 54

PG. 146

Answers

Pot Luck 3

1	Ask it a question	11	Lake Ladoga
2	Yellow	12	1940s
3	K-9	13	Ethiopia
4	2	14	Eugene O'Neill
5	Chinese	15	Bob Marley and the Wailers
6	Carrauntoohil	16	K
7	Inspector Crabtree	17	Ruritania
8	10	18	March
9	Lamb	19	Sue Townsend
10	1000	20	Poseidon

PG. 147

Pot Luck 4

1	Stefan Zweig	11	1981
2	Keith Lemon	12	100
3	Carlsberg	13	Po
4	Tribbiani	14	Hypotenuse
5	Aaron Spelling	15	The Mothers of Invention
6	Germany	16	Smaug
7	*Daddy Cool*	17	A long-running argument or fight
8	The Scorpions	18	Croft and Lloyd
9	Michael Grade	19	Cyprus
10	Northern Lights	20	11

PG. 148

Pot Luck 5

1	*A Christmas Carol*	11	Pilot
2	Hugo Weaving	12	It's spots
3	Rodgers and Hammerstein	13	*Coronation Street*
4	Bobby Farrell	14	*Grandma*
5	T.S. Eliot	15	Port Talbot
6	Twitchers	16	Wellard
7	Geller	17	Bosnia
8	Aries	18	Mexico
9	Oxford and Cambridge	19	The Wailers
10	90	20	Greece

PG. 149

Answers

Pot Luck 6

1 Aruban Florin
2 Moscow
3 Debutante
4 Mayfair
5 Bohemians
6 The Netherlands
7 Sapphire
8 3
9 Los Angeles
10 Daphne du Maurier
11 169
12 *The Scarlet Pimpernel*
13 LA Clippers
14 Nutbush
15 Al
16 Fish
17 Beard
18 Daylight Saving
19 Moscow
20 Kilderkin

PG. 150

Pot Luck 7

1 Pesetas
2 He was killed with an Ice Pick
3 1958
4 Robert Downey Jr.
5 Fear of Swallowing
6 11
7 *The Sound of Music*
8 Ike Turner
9 Tuesday
10 *Brookside*
11 His face
12 Ivor Novello
13 Jamaica
14 *On the road again*
15 13
16 April 23rd
17 *Open Sesame*
18 Geology
19 Lembit Opik
20 Canada

PG. 151

Pot Luck 8

1 January
2 Duchess of Argyll
3 Duck
4 Being Cold
5 1980
6 Pac-Man
7 Loretto School, Musselburgh,
8 Green Goddess
9 Ballast
10 Kitten
11 Stamford Raffles
12 ZZ Top
13 Geelong
14 Regents
15 Shaft
16 Italian
17 Hungarian
18 1965
19 Newton Mearns
20 A Royal Flush

PG. 152

Answers

Pot Luck 9

1. Ottawan
2. *One Thousand and One Nights*
3. Keith Harris
4. 52
5. Cindy
6. Lancashire
7. Vietnam
8. *Sapphire & Steel*
9. Banana daquiri
10. Charlotte Bronte
11. *The Fat Lady*
12. 1986
13. 34
14. 4
15. Good Friday
16. *We Don't Need Another Hero*
17. *Joey*
18. *Balamory*
19. Dave Lamb
20. Pandemonium

PG. 153

Pot Luck 10

1. Child Carrier
2. February
3. 4
4. *Heartbreak Hotel*
5. *Smash Hits*
6. Free Parking
7. The Brat Pack
8. O. Henry
9. Pluto
10. Exodus
11. Charlie Higson
12. Boo Boo
13. Staples Center
14. 15th
15. Cain
16. Gaynor Faye
17. Chanel No. 5
18. The Privy Council
19. Terry Gilliam
20. Blue

PG. 154

Pot Luck 11

1. Scafell Pike
2. *Three Little Birds*
3. Petrograd
4. Tina Turner
5. The Hard Rock Café
6. The Queen Vic
7. Rickman
8. Earl Grey
9. 18 gallons
10. Bulgaria
11. *TIME*
12. Anthony
13. India
14. Neva
15. An oligarchy
16. Cuddles the Monkey
17. Katie Morag
18. Bezel
19. Nd
20. Blackpool

PG. 155

Answers

Pot Luck 12

1	Israel	11	Gaudi
2	A type of cheese	12	March 17th
3	Bananaman	13	July
4	Long-sightedness	14	Boyzone
5	Gnasher	15	Becky Thatcher
6	*Gordon the Gopher*	16	Shirley Douglas
7	*In the Ghetto*	17	The Swiss Guard
8	Andrew Carnegie	18	France
9	The Blue Man Group	19	Dutch Guiana
10	Henley-on-Thames	20	Real Lion

PG. 156

Pot Luck 13

1	Tennis	11	Smarter than the average bear
2	Borstal	12	*The Lady*
3	Face	13	3
4	Johnnie	14	USA
5	Toby	15	Anita Dobson
6	Finnish	16	Tennessee
7	Bill Oddie	17	Toby
8	William Jefferson Blythe III	18	The Bank of England
9	Kylie Minogue	19	Geordie
10	16	20	Entemology

PG. 157

Pot Luck 14

1	Jason Donovan	11	Shirley MacLaine
2	Irving Berlin	12	Tipper
3	Green	13	Lambeth
4	Alaska	14	Elephant & Castle
5	Gerard Pique	15	Brixton
6	Goldie Hawn	16	Greenwich
7	Tim Vine	17	Southwark
8	Charlie Sheen	18	Knightsbridge
9	Melanie Griffiths	19	Sloane Rangers/ Sloaneys
10	Dakota Johnson	20	Zika Virus

PG. 158

Answers

Pot Luck 15

1. He achieved the highest freefall ever
2. Jeb Bush
3. The Arab Spring
4. Mark Duggan
5. Operation Yewtree
6. The Smiler
7. Work, rest and play
8. Hello Boys'
9. Stella Artois
10. 1979
11. Papa Doc Duvalier
12. 1998
13. Ba-ath
14. Bashar al-Assad
15. Austria
16. Access
17. American Express
18. Aquamarine
19. Brian Epstein
20. The Hosts

PG. 159

Pot Luck 16

1. Zola Budd
2. 1924
3. Serena Williams
4. The Bird's Nest
5. Aberdeen
6. Wales
7. Gold Nugget
8. Derbyshire
9. Whitby
10. Onyx
11. Fool's Gold
12. *Dear Prudence*
13. Ringo Starr
14. Abbey Road
15. George Martin
16. 9
17. 4
18. Benjamin Disraeli
19. Prince Albert
20. German

PG. 160

Pot Luck 17

1. 42
2. Martini
3. Because I'm Worth It
4. *The Bible*
5. The Jesuits
6. Mecca
7. The Amish
8. Catharism
9. *The Book of Mormon*
10. Malachi
11. Sikhism
12. Pontius Pilate
13. The Pope
14. Palm Sunday
15. John
16. French
17. Lake Van
18. There are no rivers in Saudi Arabia
19. 43560
20. New Zealand

PG. 161

Answers

Pot Luck 18

1	Wyoming	11	Pancho Villa
2	*The Star Spangled Banner*	12	Citronella
		13	Portugal
3	Bolivia	14	Norman Foster
4	North Carolina	15	Bridge
5	2015	16	Charlotte
6	Canaan Banana	17	David Beckham
7	Landscape Gardener	18	Brick Lane
8	The Alamo	19	Tower Hamlets
9	China	20	Cavendish
10	Alfie and Zoella		

PG. 162

Pot Luck 19

1	Hatfield House	11	For Him Magazine
2	Jeff Brazier	12	Claudia Schiffer
3	He jumped off a bridge	13	Jennifer Lopez and Cheryl Cole
4	A shooting accident		
5	Weather	14	John Nash
6	Narendra Modi	15	The Fortune 500
7	There are no railways in Iceland	16	Dubai
		17	Geneva
8	Ireland	18	The Black Sea
9	It is a wind	19	Every 4 years
10	Liam Payne	20	Orange Free State

PG. 163

Answers

Prime Ministers

1 1966
2 Minister
3 The Marquess of Salisbury
4 Stirling
5 3
6 Edinburgh
7 Neville Chamberlain
8 Clement Attlee
9 Australia
10 David Lloyd George
11 1
12 The Suez Crisis
13 1964
14 Jim Callaghan
15 Aberavon
16 Tony Blair
17 Ted Heath
18 Chequers
19 Andrew Bonar Law
20 Ugly Rumours

PG. 164

Real Names

1 Rowdy Roddy Piper
2 Katy Perry
3 Bottom
4 Sir Ben Kingsley
5 Alan Alda
6 Eldrick
7 Mother Teresa
8 Newton
9 Lancelot
10 Adam Faith
11 Doris Day
12 Robyn
13 David McDonald
14 Big Daddy
15 Natalie Wood
16 Bruce Lee
17 Nicholas Cage
18 George Orwell
19 Fish
20 Anton du Beke

PG. 165

Answers

Reality TV

1 Freddie Starr
2 Brian Belo
3 Nanny Pat (Brooker)
4 2010
5 Brian Belo
6 Kourtney
7 Joey Essex
8 *The Real Housewives of...*
9 *Castaway 2000*
10 Jade Goody
11 *Hallelujah* by Alexandra Burke
12 *Ex on the Beach*
13 Timlin
14 Rebecca Loos
15 *The Apprentice*
16 *Ladette to Lady*
17 The contestants thought they were competing for a date with Prince Harry, but it was only an actor
18 Ryan Seacrest
19 Shakin' Stevens
20 *Celebrity Wrestling*

PG. 166

Religion 1

1 Brigham Young
2 Evolution
3 The Square and Compass
4 13
5 666
6 Basilica
7 Eve
8 Christian Science
9 David Koresh
10 The Seventh Day Adventists
11 The Pope
12 The Book of Revelation
13 A Carpenter
14 James, son of Zebedee
15 95
16 The Ring of the Fisherman
17 William Booth
18 Geneva
19 Kali
20 John and Charles Wesley

PG. 167

Answers

Religion 2

1. Gold and Silver
2. Pope Benedict XVI
3. 1968
4. Stigmata
5. 58%
6. Quakers
7. Mary Magdalene
8. Saint Columba
9. 15th July
10. St Mungo
11. Venerable Bede
12. St Alban
13. Saint Gennaro
14. St Francis of Assisi
15. Saint Helena
16. Thomas Becket
17. St Paul
18. St Patrick
19. Winged Lion
20. Noah

PG. 168

Science

1. Yes
2. Dichlorodiphenyl-trichloroethane
3. Protons
4. NaCl (Sodium Chloride)
5. Dimitri Mendeleev
6. Strontium
7. Argentina
8. Carbon
9. Hydrogen
10. Neutrons
11. An Alkali
12. Marie Curie
13. Black
14. Nitrogen
15. Tin
16. Sand
17. Unobtanium
18. Rare Earth Elements
19. Canada
20. The Bunsen Burner

PG. 169

Answers

Soaps

1	Jimmy Corkhill	11	JR Ewing
2	John Altman	12	Pauline Fowler
3	Albert Square	13	*Neighbours*
4	4 times	14	Shona McGarty
5	Mark Fowler	15	*Dynasty*
6	*Coronation Street* (Gail Platt)	16	Chris Gascoyne
7	June Brown	17	*Family Affairs*
8	Dallas	18	Ramsay Street
9	Spencer	19	The Rovers Return
10	1994	20	Mechanic

PG. 170

Sport and Games 1

1	Plough Lane	11	A Cruyff Turn
2	Terry Butcher	12	Chris Woods
3	David Platt	13	James Milner
4	Blyth Spartans	14	Easter Road
5	Manchester United	15	Lionel Messi
6	He was Rangers first high profile Roman Catholic signing	16	64
7	Filbert Street	17	White
8	Estadio Azteca	18	Anatoly Karpov
9	North Korea	19	FIDE
10	Bari	20	Nigel Short

PG. 171

Answers

Sport and Games 2

1 24
2 Bishop
3 Cluedo
4 Chess
5 Darts
6 Trivial Pursuit
7 Contract Bridge
8 One or Two
9 Magnus Carlsen
10 Dungeons and Dragons

11 Tic-Tac-Toe
12 Snakes & Ladders
13 Buckaroo
14 The Game of Life
15 2
16 4
17 The
18 The 1920s
19 Never Have I Ever
20 Risk

PG. 172

Sport and Games 3

1 Battleships
2 Scrabble
3 Straws
4 Carl Frampton and Scott Quigg
5 Boxing
6 Red Rum
7 Kempton
8 Dick Francis
9 Chariots
10 5

11 Green
12 Shane Warne
13 Stirling Moss
14 Sébastien Foucan
15 Orlando Pirates
16 Great Triumvirate
17 Darts
18 8 yards
19 Jelena Janković
20 Golf

PG. 173

Answers

Sport and Games 4

1 The Oche
2 A Shuttlecock
3 A Puck
4 Crystal Palace
5 15
6 170
7 USA
8 Will Carling
9 Cricket
10 A Nightwatchman
11 1900
12 Namibia
13 The Buffalo Bills
14 Borussia Mönchengladbach
15 Tyson Fury
16 Gleneagles
17 Eilidh Child
18 Theo Walcott
19 Stanley Matthews
20 James Anderson

PG. 174

Sport and Games 5

1 Joe Frazier
2 Par
3 Ice Hockey
4 Los Angeles
5 15
6 4
7 Ebony Starr
8 Jimmy White
9 Fell Running
10 Joe Johnson
11 Johanna Konta
12 W.G. Grace
13 Petanque
14 Giant Haystacks
15 Snooker
16 31
17 Horse racing
18 Leighton Rees
19 Geocaching
20 Green Bay Packers

PG. 175

Answers

Sport and Games 6

1. Gymnastics
2. Pool
3. 1940s
4. 1500 metres
5. Louis Smith
6. Clive Woodward
7. Jeremy Guscott
8. None
9. Snooker
10. Speedway
11. Wimbledon Stadium
12. Bangladesh
13. Ian McGeechan
14. Rugby
15. Lawn Tennis
16. Crabbies
17. The first female presenter of Grandstand
18. Ice Hockey
19. Hawkeye
20. Frank Bruno

PG. 176

Sport and Games 7

1. Rocky Marciano
2. American Football
3. Ian Botham
4. County Durham
5. Phil Taylor
6. 3
7. Terry Venables
8. Florence Griffith-Joyner
9. 20
10. Rangers
11. Indianapolis 500
12. 2
13. Polo
14. Crab Football
15. Rebecca Adlington
16. Leicester
17. The 2000 Guineas
18. James Naismith
19. Roberto Duran
20. Ken Buchanan

PG. 177

Answers

Sport and Games 8

1 Michael Nunn
2 Ben Hollioake
3 Manchester
4 Nigel Bond
5 Baseball
6 Professional Walking
7 Finlay Calder
8 Bjorn Borg
9 Caroline Wosniacki
10 Alastair Cook
11 Martina Navratilova
12 Horse racing
13 Dario Franchitti
14 Paul di Resta
15 180
16 The Seahawks
17 Football
18 Every second year
19 Victoria Park (Ross County)
20 Gleneagles

PG. 178

The Arts

1 Leonardo Da Vinci
2 Trafalgar Square
3 *The Scream*
4 Clocks/ Watches
5 Vincent Van Gogh
6 John
7 Horses
8 The toes of his feet
9 The Scream
10 William Blake
11 Cubism
12 Paul Cezanne
13 Bernini
14 Ai Weiwei
15 Jacob Epstein
16 Émile Zola
17 Pop Art
18 L.S. Lowry
19 Rembrandt
20 *Girl with a Pearl Earring*

PG. 179

Answers

The Final Frontier

1   Ripley
2   Martin Landau
3   Battleship
4   *In space no one can hear you scream.*
5   *The Time Machine*
6   Jon Pertwee
7   T Negative
8   14
9   The Big Bang Theory
10 Apollo 11
11 Saturn
12 Mars
13 Jupiter
14 The Van Allen Belts
15 Every 29.5 days
16 Every 76 years
17 Hale-Bopp
18 University of Portsmouth
19 Columbia
20 Taikonaut

PG. 180

The Human Body

1   A Wart
2   Femur
3   In your foot
4   Their hair
5   Her leg
6   Shingles
7   The secretion of milk from the breast
8   Heartburn
9   Emphysema
10 Pulmonology
11 Your feet
12 Your brain and spinal cord
13 Aorta
14 Eyes
15 Calcium
16 The ear
17 Pancreas
18 Blood pressure
19 In the foot
20 Your pinky

PG. 181

Answers

The Royal Family

1 St Andrews
2 Pippa
3 The Stone of Destiny
4 Prince William
5 George and Charlotte
6 Princess Margaret
7 59
8 No. She doesn't need a licence to drive
9 Edward VII (10 months)
10 Fergus
11 Sophie Winkleman
12 Prince Michael of Kent
13 Peter Phillips
14 The Marquess of Milford Haven
15 St. Paul's Cathedral
16 Windsor Guildhall
17 Hillsborough Castle
18 1964
19 France
20 Althorp House

PG. 182

The World 1

1 African Elephants
2 The Pygmy Shrew
3 Mutton
4 Mustangs
5 The Platypus
6 Gorilla
7 Labrador Retriever
8 A Jenny
9 Cheetah
10 Melbourne
11 Nuuk
12 Rome
13 Reykjavik
14 Ukraine
15 True - it runs for 122 miles
16 6
17 Red, White and Blue
18 A Cedar
19 Red and Yellow
20 Finland

PG. 183

Answers

The World 2

1	Red	11	Huguenots
2	Black, White and Red	12	Napoleon
3	Green	13	*Le Grand Dauphin*
4	Black	14	Blue
5	Five	15	Pierre de Coubertin
6	Élysée Palace	16	Baron Haussmann
7	Toulouse	17	12
8	Aix-en-Provence	18	Pont de l'Alma tunnel
9	Charlatan	19	Francois
10	Biarritz	20	1922

PG. 184

The World 3

1	Douglas Hyde	11	The Severn
2	Áras an Uachtaráin	12	Vietnam
3	Trinity College, Dublin	13	River Tweed
4	Munster	14	Atlantic Ocean
5	Bari	15	The Humber
6	Florence	16	Tiber
7	Milan	17	Italy
8	Vesuvius	18	The Thames
9	Sicily	19	Vltava
10	USA	20	Jordan

PG. 185

Answers

The World 4

1	Caspian	11	Papa Noel/ Pere Noel
2	Loire	12	Venezuela (Venice)
3	Danube	13	The Vatican City
4	Tigris	14	Turkey
5	The Potomac	15	Kenya
6	Toronto	16	Icelandic Krona
7	Oil	17	Pfennigs
8	Nunavut	18	Helmut Kohl
9	Detroit	19	Munich
10	Shanghai	20	Clive of India

PG. 186

The World 5

1	Nehru	11	Greenland
2	Thugs/ Thuggee	12	The Star of David
3	Vishnu	13	Golda Meir
4	Oahu	14	Mossad
5	Montserrat	15	Poland
6	Newport	16	Mount of Olives
7	The Calf of Man	17	Yitzhak Rabin
8	Three Mile Island	18	1948
9	Jersey	19	Vulcan
10	Rhodes	20	Augustus

PG. 187

Answers

The World 6

1	Popular fish sauce	11	Harland and Wolff
2	Hannibal	12	The Isle of Man
3	Hadrian's Wall	13	Staffa
4	Fabius Maximus	14	Northern Ireland
5	Rome and Carthage	15	25
6	The Red Lion	16	Milwaukee
7	Ben Macdui	17	Geronimo
8	Glasgow	18	Crazy Horse
9	Hurricane	19	The Lakota
10	El Nino	20	Navajo

PG. 188

Toys

1	A Space Hopper	11	Hamley's
2	Tickle Me Elmo	12	Nerf
3	The Teddy Bear	13	Dr Black
4	The Gameboy	14	Tetris
5	Ken	15	Jenga
6	The Etch a Sketch	16	Lego
7	The Care Bears	17	Hoverboards
8	Old Kent Road	18	Frank Hornby
9	The Big Mouth Billy Bass	19	Tracy Island
10	Yoyo	20	Rocking Horses

PG. 189

Answers

Transport 1

1	M8	11	Heathrow
2	Routemaster	12	Glasgow Prestwick
3	Elon Musk	13	1905
4	Michael O Leary	14	The Red Flag Act
5	Wasp	15	1937
6	The Helicopter	16	The White Star Line
7	The Corolla	17	George Stephenson
8	Bicycles	18	The Segway
9	Alec Issigonis	19	Boston
10	Glasgow	20	Kawasaki

PG. 190

Transport 2

1	1959	11	Gatwick
2	Neptune's Staircase	12	A30
3	Dennis	13	The Panama Canal
4	A Pedalo	14	Bullet Train
5	Triangular	15	Left
6	Private Jets	16	Left
7	ORD	17	M6
8	JFK Airport	18	M74
9	Paris	19	Turin
10	Birkenhead	20	Seat

PG. 191

Answers

Trivia Time 1

1 *Bridget Jones: The Edge of Reason*
2 She fell off a horse
3 Tanzania
4 The Jesuits
5 Sanskrit
6 Jules
7 Measure atmospheric pressure
8 Satan
9 *Felipe VI*
10 Chief Whip
11 Hymn
12 Murmansk
13 Anton LaVey
14 Battle of Balaclava
15 Dodie Smith
16 Euston Road
17 Sachin Tendulkar
18 The Ionian Sea
19 Margaret Mitchell
20 Ostrich

PG. 192

Trivia Time 2

1 Sammy Lee
2 Optimus Prime
3 December 26th
4 1935
5 Madness
6 Kenya
7 *Always by Bon Jovi*
8 Strikes
9 Orlando
10 Jamboree
11 8 feet
12 Sachin Tendulkar
13 Wishbone
14 Variety (or Variety Club)
15 Tsar
16 Volkswagen
17 Winnipeg
18 Giacomo Puccini
19 India
20 Snowdon

PG. 193

Answers

Trivia Time 3

1 The Phillipines	11 1916
2 A moveable feast	12 Chepstow
3 1964	13 John
4 Excalibur	14 Houses
5 7	15 The Schengen Treaty
6 Alan Clark	16 *The Sun*
7 Andrew Mitchell	17 McVities
8 Gross domestic product	18 Saddam Hussein
9 A type of thick pea soup	19 78
10 Dustin Diamond	20 The 7 Years War

PG. 194

Trivia Time 4

1 Bananarama	12 Lymington
2 1990	13 *The Heat*
3 Belvedere	14 Body Odour
4 Cambodia	15 Elizabeth Stuart, Queen of Bohemia
5 Peter	16 Madison Avenue
6 Maersk Line	17 French
7 Buddhism	18 Karst
8 Groynes	19 Anne Hathaway
9 Weather phenomenon	20 By constricting (squeezing) the prey
10 2004	
11 The Druze	

PG. 195

Answers

Trivia Time 5

1 Walsall
2 Ofcom
3 The dentin
4 South Carolina
5 Harlem Globetrotters
6 Cleopatra
7 James Garner
8 Mount McKinley
9 Ronnie Knight
10 Angkor Wat, Cambodia
11 Maps
12 *The Simpsons*
13 *Live and Let Die*
14 The Dead Sea
15 Seat
16 Pharrell Williams
17 SPAM
18 *The Hatfields & The McCoys*
19 Hg
20 Yakuza

PG. 196

Trivia Time 6

1 Argentina
2 Kampuchea
3 Hafez al-Assad
4 Navigable aqueduct
5 Iceland
6 Order of the Companions of Honour
7 Field marshal
8 Harvey Nichols
9 China
10 *The Division Bell*
11 Jaipur
12 Jeanette Winterson
13 Baton Rouge
14 Ludgate
15 Amsterdam
16 Israel
17 California
18 Sir Robert Walpole
19 Tripoli
20 Swiss Cottage

PG. 197

Answers

Trivia Time 7

1. Hurricanes
2. Chef
3. Beltane
4. Martinique
5. Fitzgerald
6. John
7. Robert Ludlum
8. Harry Houdini
9. Norfolk
10. Five-year terms that can be renewed indefinitely, although none so far has held office for more than two terms
11. Migrating Cornish Miners
12. Merv Hughes
13. Africa
14. Sean Paker
15. Isle of Capri
16. The Avon
17. USA
18. A Harbour
19. Dire Straits
20. Bugs Bunny

PG. 198

Trivia Time 8

1. Lord Lieutenant
2. The Vatican, Monaco, San Marino and Andorra
3. Zulu
4. Nitrogen
5. Osborne House
6. 1978
7. Valetta
8. Bethlehem
9. Kuna
10. WW1
11. A 99
12. Stockport
13. James Braid
14. Peggy
15. Cuckoos
16. Trinity College, Dublin
17. Boy George
18. Jeff Bezos
19. Albedo
20. 1837

PG. 199

Answers

Trivia Time 9

1 French
2 Millennium Bridge
3 *Jai Ho*
4 80 minutes
5 He wore an eyepatch
6 Georges Simenon
7 Mycroft
8 Saltwood Castle
9 Hillbillys
10 Matt Groening
11 Arsenal
12 Hajj
13 Essex
14 Dar es Salaam
15 Montserrat
16 American
17 Hamburg
18 Bahrain
19 Mount Kenya
20 Old Father Time

PG. 200

Trivia Time 10

1 1999
2 *Transformers: Age of Extinction*
3 1928
4 Tulliallan Castle
5 Australia
6 Mary Tourtel
7 Ra
8 *Freckleface Strawberry*
9 1982
10 An Usher
11 Electrical Appliances
12 St Peter's Basilica
13 Picketing
14 Ford
15 Alexandria
16 Fort Sumter
17 Sharia Law
18 Vitamin B12
19 Peter
20 Rowan Atkinson

PG. 201

Answers

Trivia Time 11

1	Holyhead	11	John duPont
2	Robert De Niro	12	Jai ho
3	Seth MacFarlane	13	Banksy
4	1972	14	Walt Disney
5	None	15	Jethro
6	Rio Grande	16	Brutalism
7	Foxcatcher	17	Rotterdam
8	East Cowes	18	Muslim Spain
9	Tottenham Hotspur	19	Triads
10	Oman (since 1970)	20	A Hat

PG. 202

Trivia Time 12

1	Horror	11	Battle of Camlann
2	Benin	12	Lizzy Yarnold
3	90 minutes	13	Aylesbury
4	Snowy	14	Halloween, October 31st
5	A Horse	15	The British Library
6	Edgar Allan Poe	16	Adam Hills
7	Tenerife	17	The Kosovan War
8	Exxon Mobil	18	Thank You & Goodbye
9	Type of Castle	19	Pol Pot
10	The Ottoman Empire	20	Julianne Moore

PG. 203

Answers

Trivia Time 13

1 *The Guinness Book of World Records*
2 Gypsies and Travellers
3 Flying Pickets
4 Debenhams
5 The Atacama Desert
6 Laos
7 Robert Gibb
8 Pope Benedict XVI
9 Fortress or Stronghold
10 Battle of Saltley Gate
11 Monty Don
12 1980
13 Penguin
14 April
15 Betting and Gambling
16 Chuck Yeager
17 An Ultimatum
18 JPMorgan Chase
19 Justin Timberlake
20 6

PG. 204

Trivia Time 14

1 Aintree
2 Queen Nefertiti
3 Bratva
4 Montserrat Caballé
5 Ulster Fry
6 The Gold Standard
7 Public Display of Affection
8 Nairobi
9 A large Bomber Aircraft
10 Edinburgh's
11 Young deer
12 Yvette Fielding
13 The Dambusters Raid
14 *Casino Royale*
15 Pub in Nottingham
16 Warren Buffett
17 Matt Damon
18 O
19 Wales
20 Virgin of Montserrat

PG. 205

Answers

Trivia Time 15

1 Denali/ Mt McKinley
2 Mr Whippy Ice Cream
3 Jersey
4 10
5 Sunni
6 Ashes to Ashes
7 Scotland
8 Elephant
9 A building at the centre of Islam's most sacredmosque, Al-Masjid al-Haram
10 Widnes
11 Dr Watson
12 Igneous, Sedimentary and Metamorphic
13 Castel Gandolfo
14 Belgian
15 Gary Neville
16 Hammer
17 Nairobi
18 The state of Egypt
19 Jordi
20 Geoffrey of Monmouth

PG. 206

Trivia Time 16

1 Paternoster Square
2 Hampton Court Maze
3 Sachsgate
4 Whips
5 Joseph M. Scriven
6 Inuit
7 Matt Damon
8 Victor Emmanuel II
9 South Pole
10 Scotland
11 Scottish
12 The Indian Navy
13 No
14 Yes
15 Yes
16 Up-market
17 Yes
18 Hot
19 South Korea
20 Bruce Lee

PG. 207

Answers

Trivia Time 17

1 Bruce Dern
2 Robert Redford
3 He was thrown from his horse
4 *Billy Budd*
5 8 times
6 Duncan Norvelle
7 Vicky Pollard
8 Leslie Phillips
9 Stu Francis
10 88
11 Architect
12 Joiner
13 Orderly
14 Laelaps
15 Icarus
16 Helots
17 The Ferryman of Hades
18 Cerberus
19 Alexandria
20 Lebanon

PG. 208

True Crime

1 Amanda Knox
2 DB Cooper
3 Charles Manson
4 Jimmy Hoffa
5 Judge Ito
6 Drinking the Kool-Aid
7 Peter Anthony Allen and Gwynne Owen Evans
8 Ronnie Biggs
9 Jack Ruby
10 Ian Huntley
11 Jerry Lee Lewis
12 The Angry Brigade
13 Jacqueline Hill
14 London
15 Graverobbers
16 Austria
17 Bangui
18 Shannon Matthews
19 Shoplifting
20 Ruth Ellis

PG. 209

Answers

TV 1

1	You Bet!	11	Sam Heughan
2	Richard Hammond	12	Antiques Dealer
3	Jeopardy!	13	Yvette Fielding
4	Wheel of Fortune	14	Gok Wan
5	Big Break	15	Barbara
6	All Clued Up	16	295
7	Gladiators	17	Dragon's Den
8	Take Me Out	18	Konnie Huq
9	The Simple Life	19	Linda Gray
10	His Teeth	20	Ian McShane

PG. 210

TV 2

1	Cheers	11	Cabot Cove
2	Dave	12	Dara O Briain
3	Stephen Graham	13	House of Fools
4	Alex Jones	14	Peep Show
5	Bruce Springsteen	15	Mary Berry and Paul Hollywood
6	Coronation Street	16	Jamie Oliver
7	Aunt Sally	17	John Hurt
8	Sesame Street	18	The X-Files
9	Stefan Dennis	19	Twin Peaks
10	Steve Brookstein	20	Lost

PG. 211

Answers

TV 3

1	MASH	11	Moonlighting
2	Dancing With the Stars	12	Paddy McGuinness
3	Darrowby	13	Chuck Lorre
4	KARR	14	Boy George
5	Jay Silverheels	15	Inspector Morse
6	1928	16	Soccer Saturday
7	Dennis Potter	17	Matt le Blanc
8	Julia Bradbury	18	Mary Whitehouse
9	A fracas with the show's producer	19	The Mary Whitehouse Experience
10	Annabel Croft	20	The House of Eliott

PG. 212

TV 4

1	1969	11	The Eggheads
2	Gomez	12	William G Stewart
3	Airwolf	13	Lou Ferrigno
4	Come Dine With Me	14	Anton du Beke and Dale Winton
5	ITV2	15	Alex Norton
6	Going Live	16	The History Channel
7	Paul Giamatti	17	Natasha Kaplinsky
8	Po	18	Maplins
9	Tony Shalhoub	19	Crossbow
10	Oz	20	1997

PG. 213

Answers

TV 5

1	Gladiators	11	Keith Lemon
2	Splash!	12	Lloyd Grossman
3	Jenni Falconer	13	Felicity Kendal
4	Jim Henson	14	Nile Rodgers
5	4	15	Russia Today
6	John Leslie	16	Byker Grove
7	John Hurt	17	Skinner
8	Kevin Clifton	18	Victoria Coren Mitchell
9	Diversity	19	Tabitha
10	Neighbours	20	6

PG. 214

TV 6

1	Brighton Belles	11	Minder
2	Gogglebox	12	Justin Fletcher
3	Columbo	13	Challenge TV
4	Homeland	14	Carol Smilie
5	Hannibal Smith	15	DIY SOS
6	Gregor Fisher	16	Jack Klugman
7	The Royle Family	17	Richard Whiteley
8	The Wombles	18	House
9	All I'm a Celebrity winners	19	The Kennedy's
10	Frank Butcher	20	Channel 4

PG. 215

Answers

UK Places

1	Liverpool	11	Cwmbran
2	Paddy's WigWam	12	Cramlington
3	Domesday Book	13	13 times
4	Aldershot	14	Inverness
5	Altrincham	15	Lytham
6	Keswick	16	Walsingham
7	Windsor	17	Falkirk
8	Milton Keynes	18	Bolsover
9	Stevenage	19	Omagh
10	Amesbury	20	Ryde

PG. 216

USA 1

1	Rhode Island	11	Virginia
2	Florida	12	West Point
3	Alcatraz	13	8
4	Harvard	14	1993
5	Merv Griffin	15	South Dakota
6	Baltimore	16	Houston
7	Scottsdale, Arizona	17	New York
8	Robert Leroy Parker	18	The Washington Monument
9	1931	19	Alex Haley
10	Mexico	20	Roe V Wade

PG. 217

Answers

USA 2

1	Detroit	11	Carson City
2	Chesapeake Bay	12	Billy Graham
3	Pyramid	13	2001
4	New Orleans	14	Las Vegas
5	Texas	15	Sacramento
6	SoHo	16	Chicago
7	Little Italy	17	1930s
8	Queens	18	Turkey
9	Las Vegas	19	Los Angeles
10	Juilliard School	20	The Bronx

PG. 218

War

1	Enola Gay	11	116 years
2	Saigon	12	The Mongols
3	A semi-auotmatic assualt rifle	13	The Cold War
4	Ho Chi Minh	14	Saudi Arabia
5	In your garden	15	Air Raid Patrol
6	The Treaty of Paris	16	1918
7	Japan	17	Mons
8	1848	18	Admiral Jellicoe
9	Yalta	19	Vietnam War
10	The Second Boer War	20	Battle of El Alamein

PG. 219

Answers

Who was born first?

1	Holly Willoughby	11	Jade Goody
2	Jeremy Corbyn	12	Ian Brady
3	Nigel Mansell	13	Miley Cyrus
4	Winston Churchill	14	Queen Elizabeth II
5	Donald Trump	15	Gordon Brown
6	Ronald Reagan	16	Jamie Oliver
7	Kate Middleton	17	Larry Hagman
8	Alan Sugar	18	Olivia Newton-John
9	Diego Maradonna	19	JMW Turner
10	Freddie Mercury	20	Stephen Fry

PG. 220

WW2

1	Chiang Kai-shek	11	The Operation Valkyrie attempt on Hitler's life
2	December 7th, 1941	12	Scotland
3	Operation Overlord	13	The Phoney War
4	Fuhrer	14	18 to 41
5	The Red Army	15	'Sink Ships'
6	Heinrich Himmler	16	The Free Polish
7	Blitzkrieg	17	The Chindits
8	The Battle of the Bulge	18	Vichy
9	Crete	19	The Channel Islands
10	Benito Mussolini	20	1987

PG. 221